THE MAGIC OF HERBS

Recently published in Corgi Mini-Books

AUDREY WYNNE HATFIELD
F.R.H.S.

THE MAGIC OF HERBS

A MINI-BOOK BY CORGI

THE MAGIC OF HERBS

A MINI-BOOK   552 76345 4

PRINTING HISTORY
Mini-Book Edition published 1970
Mini-Book Edition reprinted 1971
Copyright © 1970 Audrey Wynne Hatfield

Mini-Books are published by
Transworld Publishers Ltd., Cavendish House,
57–59 Uxbridge Road, Ealing, London, W.5.
Made and printed in Great Britain by
Fletcher & Son Ltd, Norwich

For Sheila Olive Ball

CONTENTS

INTRODUCTION

The magic of herbs is in their physical make-up, and the beneficial effect on our own. In reality the term 'herb' applies to all plants, but many people today believe it means only the few culinary types that have remained in our impoverished menus, such as Mint for sauce and to flavour new potatoes, Sage and Thyme for stuffings, Parsley that is also used for sauce, or for trimmings along with Watercress; and these garnishing sprays are usually discarded, though the Parsley and the Watercress would probably be of more value to the diner's health than the dish they decorate: and of course there is Garlic for those who like it. These few herbs are too often valued only for their pleasant flavours, scarcely ever for the bonus of their health-giving qualities.

If we realise that plants are the most important part of our natural food it is obvious that so scanty a knowledge of their possibilities is our loss and our handicap. But when we know something of their real worth we can enrich our culinary achievements not only with their various flavours but also with their wholesome medicines: the ancients used them to treat all their diseases, and they had to base their medical knowledge on results experienced and handed down. But our modern laboratory techniques can tell us why some plants were, and still are, effective. Their beneficial constituents are tracked down by the research chemists, sometimes to be reproduced synthetically to provide medicines to cope with our present-day needs. So if we know the plants which contain such virtues, and if we regularly consume them, we get their help at first hand and avoid the prevalent deficiencies, which are often the cause of serious ailments. Herbs will also give us welcome relief in many cases of illness.

If we have a garden we should grow certain herbs which, apart from their values, are beautiful plants and are especially delicious when freshly gathered: and we can exploit many of the weeds which are surprisingly beneficial. But whatever our situation, almost all the curative and culinary types (properly dried) can be bought from good Health Food stores. So long as we know the kinds we require for our various purposes, we need never lack herbs. I wish this book to be a simple, useful guide to the proper enjoyment of herbal magic: it has to be brief, but it must contain a fair selection of the plants which are known to benefit our health, our looks and our tempers.

Herbs are vastly important because a plant growing from the soil with light rays above is capable of selecting and transforming for its own growth all the basic materials upon which all other life also depends; it renders them into foods required by animals and man, which they could not themselves assimilate. Also from the earth, plants can take in and convert into assimilable forms the many minerals that are necessary to our well-being, such as iron, copper—some have been known to take up gold if it is handy—with all the essential chemicals we call 'trace elements'. Plants alone are our original source of vitamins, carbohydrates, proteins, oils and other necessities, even though we may get them second-hand from animal flesh; or from fish who live on the minute plants peculiar to water, for these, too, assimilate the essential elements that are washed down from the land into rivers, lakes and seas.

Without vegetation we would not be here, for we would have to eat rocks and chew sand, washed down with rain-water or lifeless seawater in order to obtain the things our bodies need. Only vegetation can get sustenance from the basic rocks which have, for thousands of millions of years, undergone cycles of life and decay, thereby turning into soil on which vegetation lives, and from which it supports all animal life—and ourselves.

Our choice of the herbs, or plants, we require for our different purposes depends upon *their* particular needs and capacities for selecting, transforming and, in some cases, storing for their own needs, the essentials which happen to be desirable for our own.

The parts of plants which are useful to us depend on the season of growth—for instance, in spring and summer we filch the leaves that are busily absorbing sunlight and circulating all the vibrant juices rushing to achieve their functions. We may take the flowers filled with nectar and pollen. Actually many flowers have health-giving properties, such as the Marigold, Borage, Sweet Pea, Violet, Nasturtium,

Chrysanthemum petals. They should be served in salads, and they look lovely arranged on top of the greenery. Of course, the obvious way to get more of their virtues is by eating the stuff collected by bees, pure honey, which is a perfect 'herbal' food and sweetening, and is unadulterated with villainous white sugar.

Later, we take the seeds, the fruits, the little packages of concentrated food made ready to supply the first important nourishment needed by the infant seedling.

When a plant that is an annual (enduring only for one year like a Sweet Pea) has accomplished its fruiting it dies; but a perennial plant, which comes up year after year, becomes dormant in winter. Such a plant may be of the type which grows from a bulb, a tuber, a tap-root or rhizome—for example, an Onion, Shallot, Garlic; Potato, Carrot, Dandelion; or the troublesome weed, Couchgrass, whose rhizomatic roots are a famous treatment for bladder and kidney disorders and are claimed by herbalists to be a natural cure for cystitis. In autumn such plants will have accumulated for next season's growth a vast store of natural starches and sugars with other excellent things in their swollen root stocks—and these we take for our winter use.

Rhubarb is an exceptional plant, the leaves, being full of oxalate, are harmful, but the luscious stems are free of the irritant, and may be eaten with impunity. Potatoes, too, have harmful leaves and fruits, but their roots are nutritious.

For better understanding I have quoted some popular root vegetables, but this book is concerned only with the virtuous plants we call herbs, whether medicinal or culinary, which are necessary to our well-being. Especially today, when many of us enjoy a very high protein diet—meat, eggs, cheese—which is deficient in the vitamins and trace elements, unless accompanied by vegetables and fruits and by a fair amount of liquid intake. My particular plea for the daily drinking of herb teas are the tisanes, at least half a pint a day. These should be varied during the week and be made from two or three kinds of plants, as the leaves appear to work better when in company than when alone with their own kind.

From these herb infusions we can get most of the benefits the plants have to offer; the chlorophyll that keeps the blood stream happy and prosperous; the vitamins and other necessities with which we can avoid dietary deficiencies. I have given a list of the ailments which certain plants are especially equipped to relieve; and to make curative or corrective infusions, two or three kinds of plants with similar references should be used.

But for general well-being the herbs should be chosen for their effect on most of the organs and to maintain their healthy functioning; as for the bladder, kidneys, liver, stomach, blood circulation—with a bias towards one's own weaknesses. For myself, I use three or four Dandelion leaves in all my mixtures to be sure of their iron and other things.

I have proved the value of herbs—but I am not advocating self-treatment with them for any serious illness, when a doctor must be consulted. But their daily use will help to avoid a great many troubles.

Herbs work rather slowly, but their good effects are worth a little patient persistence.

AGRIMONY   *Agrimonia eupatoria*

Agrimony, Church steeples, Sticklewort, is a venerable old herb growing in many country districts. It is recognisable by its stiff flowering stems that are topped by a tapering spiral of tiny pale yellow flowers shaped like miniature wild roses. There are two species of this plant: one grows anywhere; the other cannot tolerate a chalky soil—but it has the added attraction of being sweetly scented in all its parts, the root and the pretty leaflets smell of apricots.

The whole plant is used in herbal treatments, where its constituents will prove helpful. These are astringent and tonic; they act upon the kidneys, and they have the power to open obstructions in the glands and pores. An infusion made by pouring a pint of boiling water over a handful of the fresh herb, or 1 oz of the dried herb, is an excellent gargle for a sore or relaxed throat; half a teacupful taken three or four times a day remedies relaxed bowels and simple diarrhoea; and sweetened with a little honey, it soothes coughs and colds. This concoction is recommended for such skin troubles as eruptions, acne and eczema, and should be taken three times a day in wineglassful doses until the disease clears up—which may take several months.

A very good wine can be brewed from Agrimony which is both pleasurable and helpful as a cure for colds.

ANGELICA   *Angelica archangelica*

This giant among medicinal and culinary herbs was once credited as being the comforter of all man's diseases, and was grown everywhere for its various uses. The plant resembles a huge hemlock, but with bright green tender leaves: its large umbels of flowers are greenish-white in colour and are produced on thick stems, which can rise up to six feet. The whole of this plant is aromatic, entirely edible and useful; and it should be in every garden. It is a biennial that dies after the flowers have produced their seeds—but if the flower stems are cut down before maturing the plant will try again another year, and it is easily raised from seed. As an example of its flavouring capabilities, the muscatel flavour of some Rhine wines is enhanced by the use of Angelica; both its roots and seeds are ingredients in the preparation of the liqueur Chartreuse, and other well-known drinks.

Angelica's complex constituents of oils, resins, acids give their flavour, scent and wholesome healing virtues to all parts of the plant. It is a mild stimulant; good for the heart, cooling in feverish complaints and helpful to the kidneys; it is excellent for relieving coughs, bronchial catarrh, pleurisy, wind, colic, flatulence and rheumatism. The tea is made by infusing 1 oz of the fresh root bruised, or 1 oz of the dried herb, with 1 pint of boiling water. This should be taken frequently in wineglassful doses. But the seeds and the leaves, fresh or dried, can be blended with other herbs in the herb teas for daily use. Angelica leaves alone make a tea that is a real pick-me-up, and whose effect is quickly appreciated.

As a culinary herb, Angelica's young tender stems are good chopped into a salad: the mid-ribs of the leaves, first blanched, then boiled, are delicious eaten like celery. Angelica stalks cooked with rhubarb correct its tartness and make the dish palatable and enjoyable for people who cannot relish rhubarb alone. The Angelica stems may either be cut like the rhubarb or they may be cooked in lengths and removed before serving.

The plant is not difficult to grow, it likes a partly shaded position and reasonably good soil.

Angelica is not suitable for anyone suffering from diabetes, as it increases the sugar content in the urine.

ANISEED   *Pimpinella anisum*

Aniseed or anise is an attractive annual herb for a garden where it can be given a warm sunny bed of light, dryish soil. The useful seeds do not often ripen in cold wet English summers, but the plants are worth growing for the bright green foliage, which varies from shapely leaves to feathery leaflets; and these are good in salads, stews and soups and in certain stuffings for game. The umbrellas of white blossoms resemble those borne by Sweet Cicely, and the whole plant has much the same familiar Aniseed scent and flavour.

This is a plant of ancient associations, and was once made into a popular perfume; and a medication for several ills. It was also employed in many dishes where the flavour was liked and its digestive virtues were appreciated. It is still used a great deal in France and Spain, not only to flavour cakes and confectionery but also in the making of such liqueurs as the delicious Anisette.

The constituents of Aniseed, in particular its volatile oil, make it a powerful antiseptic that will mitigate the fermentation of food when digestion is slow, weak or harassed: it corrects acidity and flatulence. For its ability to break up and liquefy bronchial secretions, Aniseed is used in the mixing of many cough medicines and lozenges. And the tea infused from its leaves or seeds has the same useful effect.

An infusion of a small bunch of fresh leaves with a pint of boiling water is an excellent strengthener of the digestion, and an easer of coughs; a few leaves should sometimes be put into the daily herb tea to add Aniseed's virtues to the brew.

The seeds, which are obtained from most good herb shops, are the most popular part of this herb, and a very useful remedial tea is infused by pouring half a pint of boiling water on two teaspoonfuls of bruised seeds: this is sweetened with a little honey, and is especially good for infants suffering from catarrh. It is given cold in frequent doses of one to three teaspoonfuls. A stronger infusion is advised for grown-ups.

Jollier uses for the seeds are as flavouring for cakes, buns and biscuits. And as a spicy condiment when pounded into a pepper-like powder. This 'pepper' makes a tasty shrimp dish to be eaten with salad. For this, shell a pint of shrimps; mix them with a dressing of oil, vinegar, lemon juice and a little made mustard, and add a tablespoonful of minced mixed herbs—Parsley, Chives, Tarragon and Chervil; then blend the mixture with a wineglassful of Sherry and a little salt and Aniseed pepper to taste.

AVENS _Geum urbanum_

For its virtues, the Avens was called by the ancient physicians Herba Benedicta—Herb Bennet. They credited the plant as being the antidote for all poisons, the medicine for many ailments and the charm to scare away the devil.

Avens is a familiar wild plant with slender wiry stems growing up to 2 feet high, slightly branching and topped with little yellow blossoms like those of a wild Strawberry. The hairy darkish leaves are borne on long stalks and arranged along the stem in two or three pairs of large toothed leaflets. All the plant is virtuous, and its ancient medicinal reputation is still, in part, valid. The herb's action is astringent, toning and healing, and it will stop bleeding. The astringent action makes it a useful remedy in attacks of diarrhoea and of dysenteries which may be caused by unsuitable food, in which case the herb will also deal with the upsets caused to the liver and stomach. This is a herbalist's remedy for leucorrhoea and for agues. Avens tea will be found to be a comforting and healing gargle for a sore throat, and a curative drink to relieve a chill or cold and to cure the resulting catarrh.

The tea is made by infusing 1 oz of the powdered herb or root, with 1 pint of boiling water. This is a pleasant drink with a rather clove-like taste, and it should be taken (strained) in wineglassful doses three or four times a day during the illness. And its continued use will help the patient to recover from the usual weakness and debility caused by the ailment. Apart from being a specific medicine, Avens tea should be taken as a springtime pick-me-up. For this infusion, half a teaspoonful of the dried herb is used to 1 pint of boiling water.

This same infusion makes an excellent astringent skin lotion for clearing the complexion of spots, sunburn, freckles and other blemishes, and will help to refine coarse pores.

The dried herb is stocked by good herb shops.

BALM   *Melissa officinalis*

Lemon Balm, Cure-all, the herb to keep the memory and strengthen the brain—so thought the old herbalists, and they believed it would chase away melancholy. This old-fashioned herb with rich green heart-shaped leaves is in many gardens, but seldom is it appreciated except for plucking a sweetly lemon-scented leaf in passing, and calling the Balm, lemon Verbena! But Balm is a hardy friendly plant, easy to cultivate and delightful to use. Its qualities are useful for calming palpitations; it increases the appetite and helps the digestion and circulation; it has a cooling effect and is refreshing for feverish patients suffering from catarrh or influenza—and it makes an equally cooling and refreshing drink for anyone in hot weather.

To make the tea, infuse three or four sprays of fresh leaves whenever possible, or 1 oz of dried ones, in a pint of boiling water. For the summer drink use fresh leaves, a little lemon juice or peel may be added—with honey.

As a culinary herb it is good chopped fine in salads; the whole leaves go well in stews and casseroles, and minced leaves for stuffings will impart a faint lemon flavour.

The leaves are good for pot-pourri mixtures, as they dry well and retain their scent for a long time.

Balm is a perennial and will grow in any reasonably good soil; but it hates manure—once it is established in a garden the seedlings will come up in odd places and make good-looking foliage plants, and provide a number of leaf-sprays to be enjoyed.

BASIL   *Ocymum basilicum*

Sweet Basil, Clove-scented Basil, was once used to make the royal perfumes, unguents and medicines. The plant is a tender annual that should be sown under glass in March to be planted outside in June; or it may be sown outside in May in a sunny sheltered bed of rich soil. The plant reaches a height of about 2 feet, with 1-inch-long pointed leaves spotted on the underside with oil glands: they are smooth and cool to touch and delightfully fragrant.

Basil's constituents make it a useful herb for aiding the digestion, relieving flatulence, calming the nerves, and it has cooling properties.

For these attributes, and for its delightful flavour, a few leaves of Sweet Basil should be added to the daily herb tea. But it is principally as a culinary asset that Basil is now valued. It is a favourite herb of French cooks, and was much fancied by English cooks from the Middle Ages until the nineteenth century. Two centuries ago Basil was the flavouring herb which made Fetter Lane sausages so famous that people were enticed from all parts of London to buy them.

As a culinary herb, Basil is delicious sprinkled in salads; and in stuffings, stews, casseroles, soups, cheese dishes, egg dishes, sauces, herb butters, minces, rissoles and sausages, which are excellent when the meat is taken out of the skins and mixed with finely chopped Basil—or sage and thyme— then returned to the skin to be cooked. If the sausage skin is too flimsy the seasoned meat may be rolled into shape and fried nude.

Basil is available, dried, from all good herb stores, and it really is a valuable seasoning.

Sweet Bay is a small tree worthy of any garden for its dark green, aromatic, glossy evergreen leaves—which once made the crowns for heroes, poets and other celebrities—and nowadays are used to flavour our tastiest dishes, whether savoury or sweet. But apart from enjoying its culinary virtues, the Bay tree is an asset to the garden—or it will grow in a tub on a veranda or terrace, and is often seen standing outside a restaurant.

Bay's medicinal virtues were once exploited, but nowadays they are mainly to be had from its use as a flavouring herb which comforts the stomach and promotes the appetite. Two or three leaves will enrich the taste of a large stew or casserole, jugged hare or rabbit; and a leaf should be laid on any roasting joint; and on baking fish. Bay leaves are used in pickling and sousing. Two leaves floating on a milk pudding or baked egg custard will impart a very pleasant flavour to the dish: and to flavour egg custard sauce, first put 1 or 2 Bay leaves into the milk and bring it to the boil; then let it cool and remove the leaves before blending the custard.

The shrub will grow in some shade so long as it is protected from cold winter winds. It needs a good well-drained soil and an occasional feed of compost.

The dried leaves are available at any good herb shop.

BORAGE

Borago officinalis

'Sprigs of Borage are of known virtue to revive the hypochondriac and cheer the hard student,' wrote Sir John Evelyn in the seventeenth century. Borage is a lovely herb, entirely pleasurable in all its parts. In the garden the stiff silvery hairs bristling from stem, leaf and calyx, shimmering in the sunlight, make a fair setting for the bright blue star-shaped flowers with their dramatic purple-black cones of anthers. Bees revel in their rich honey yield, so that Borage in a garden helps to ensure the fertilisation of fruits.

This herb's constituents include potassium and calcium, with other mineral acids: the fresh plant contains a high percentage, and the dried a lesser amount, of nitrate of potash. The stems and leaves when boiled supply nitrate and salt, and these saline qualities are Borage's valuable wholesome properties, which are greater than in most vegetables. As a culinary herb, the stems and leaves make a virtuous *vegetable dish*. For this; wash the leaves and put them dripping wet into a saucepan with only a tablespoonful of water and a knob of butter or margarine; stir them around while cooking over a low heat, to prevent their burning. When tender, strain the mass, season with a dash of pepper—no salt, add a little more butter if required and serve hot with a sprinkling of chopped chives or spring onion, which will improve the dish. The liquid should not be wasted, it contains valuable nitre and salt, it can be added to the daily brew of herb tea, or to soup, gravy or sauce.

The young and tender, cucumber-flavoured leaves, and the edible flowers, are good in *salads*. And the ever-popular fashion of floating Borage sprays in wine-cups and summer drinks is based on their cooling and invigorating effect— apart from their attraction when bubbles collect, bejewelling the hairs.

Medicinally, Borage is a kidney and bladder herb; it soothes the digestive organs; soothes the bronchials; cools feverish conditions. It makes a poultice for inflamed swellings. And the tea supplies the valuable elements not only for combating such complaints but also to remedy certain diet deficiencies. This is infused with 1 oz of fresh leaves, or 1 teaspoonful of dried, to 1 pint of boiling water.

For the garden, a packet of Borage seed will give pleasure and comfort for many years. The plant is a hardy annual 2 feet tall, and when established in a garden it sows its own seeds.

The dried herb is obtainable from the best herb shops.

BUCHU   *Barosma betulina*

Buchu, Bucku the Hottentots call this estimable herb with which they perfume their bodies and cure many of their ailments. This is an attractive, small, bushy plant that is found only in the south-western regions of Cape Colony. It grows there in profusion, revelling on dry sunny hillsides, but it refuses to grow anywhere else with any signs of enjoyment: other than a few captive specimens that are pampered in a greenhouse at Kew Gardens. So, as all the efforts to cultivate it for commerce in other parts of the world have failed, the supplies from South Africa are so valuable that the plant colonies have had to be rigorously protected. Buchu leaves are an ingredient in several proprietary medicines in America and elsewhere.

The African natives' knowledge of their 'Bucku's' curative properties probably goes back many thousands of years, and the plant's introduction into European medicine dates from 1790, so that Buchu's remedial reputation is based on a great deal of medical experience.

Buchu is related to Rue, it bears small whitish flowers and its thick, glossy, pale green leaves are spangled with round oil glands which give them a pungent aromatic taste and a strong Rue-like scent. The herb's constituents include a volatile oil, resin, gum, albumen, mucilage and the antiseptic diosphenol that is largely responsible for the cures Buchu achieves: there is also rutin, which is one of the common Rue's assets. This complex directly affects the urinary organs and makes the herb especially useful in the treatment of cases with gravel, inflammation and catarrh of the bladder or kidneys. It has a restorative effect on that organ, relieving irritation and acidity, it increases the flow of urine when necessary, and reduces the output if it is too profuse. It reduces prostatic swelling and is the remedy most recommended for the relief of mild cystitis, urethritis and nephritis. This is a stimulant and is also a treatment for stomach troubles.

An infusion of this valuable herb is made by pouring 1 pint of boiling water over 1 oz of dried Buchu leaves—kept covered to preserve the steam; this is taken in wineglassful doses three or four times a day.

The solid extract is available as Buchu pills and tablets: or it is incorporated in specific medicines.

The dried leaves for infusions made at home are sold by most herbalists.

BUCKWHEAT   *Fagopyrum esculentum*
                                  Polygonum Fagopyrum

Buckwheat, or Saracen Corn, was so called after the Crusaders brought the plant back to Europe from its native Asia, where it was cultivated as a bread-corn. This is quite an attractive annual that is sometimes planted in British gardens for the sake of its two-foot-high, knotted, thick green or red-tinged hollow stems, the lateral branches growing from the joints with fresh-green, heart-shaped leaves and panicles of pretty, pale pink, scented flowers. In England Buckwheat is cultivated as a crop, particularly in the fens; it is planted in game preserves as a favourite food of pheasants; they eat the grains in autumn and shelter among the withered plants in winter. In Northern Europe and North America Buckwheat is widely sown for milling into flour to make the tasty, rather violet-coloured cakes that are popular for breakfast, with Maple syrup. The Germans favour Buckwheat pottage, and they brew beer and make cordials

27

from the grain. In various countries it is famed as a bee-food, especially in Russia, where they collect great quantities of the very pleasantly flavoured Buckwheat honey.

The nuts—'seeds'—have a tough skin enclosing the soft kernel, and they resemble Beechnuts.

Buckwheat comes into the list of modern curative herbs because of the high content of rutic acid that is found in the leaves and flowers—far higher than that of the common Rue, Buchu or the small amount in Holly. This chemical is powerfully effective for reducing high blood pressure and for renewing the vitality of the blood stream when it is becoming impaired by advancing age, for which it provides a preventive assurance. It is prescribed for the correction of hardening arteries, of varicose veins and for circulation defects which are shown by chilblains.

The pure form of rutin is available from the products sold in Health Food Stores as tablets, which can be swallowed or infused as a curative tea.

BURDOCK   *Arcticum lappa*

Burdock is a very common 'weed' to be found by the road-side, by derelict buildings and in dampish ditches and other waste places. It grows from 3 to 4 feet tall, with branching stems and large heart-shaped pale green leaves, which are covered with fine grey down on the undersides. The round purplish flower-heads are held in a ball of hooked bristles which ensure the fruit burrs a good hold on any animal or human who comes near the herb in late summer.

This plant is popularly called 'Dock' on account of its huge leaves, but unlike the true Docks, all its parts are not only edible and wholesome but Burdock is one of the most important of medicinal herbs and is used in the herbal pills and mixtures that are blended for purifying the blood and for other curative treatments.

As a beneficial culinary plant containing mineral nutrients necessary to safeguard health—and free for the cutting from almost any piece of waste ground—Burdock's stalks should be taken before the flowers are open, and when peeled of their tough rind and boiled they make a delicate asparagus-flavoured vegetable dish to be served with melted butter or margarine. They are good, too, served as a raw salad with an oil and vinegar dressing.

The roots, the leaves and the fruits, 'seeds', are all used medicinally for domestic treatments, and the plant's constituents make it a valuable infusion, decoction, lotion or poultice for many diseases. It is an astringent; an alterative that quickens the renewal of damaged tissues to enable them to function efficiently: it acts sympathetically on the bladder and kidneys; it will promote perspiration when desirable, through the pores and glands. Burdock has a sound reputation for curing skin diseases and has effectively tackled cases of eczema. It makes a useful medicine to relieve boils and rheumatism.

A decoction of the root and seeds is made from 1 oz (of the dried) to $1\frac{1}{2}$ pints of water and boiled down to 1 pint.

This is to be taken in wineglassful doses four times a day before meals. For skin and kidney troubles the decoction is more effective when made from the seeds only, no root.

An infusion of the fresh or dried leaves, 1 oz to a pint of boiling water, is recommended as a tea to be taken for stomach upsets and for indigestion, and it makes a good lotion for curing ulcers and scaly sores.

The leaves made into a poultice can be applied, externally, to relieve gouty swellings, bruises or any inflamed surfaces.

The dried Burdock can be obtained from herbal stores.

CARAWAY   *Carum carvi*

Caraway is a pretty biennial for the garden, where it produces its fruit 'seeds' the next year after the seeds are sown; and these ripen best when in a sunny, warm situation. It grows about 2 feet high and is clothed with ferny aromatic leaves, and with its umbels of tiny white flowers it resembles a refined Cow Parsley. Caraway is worth growing for the foliage as well as for the seeds, which seem to be more delicious when home-grown. Of course they are supplied by any grocery or health food store (though their quality varies). But the foliage can only be enjoyed from a garden. The leaves enrich any stew, casserole or salad, especially potato salad, and cabbage and apple coleslaw; and a Caraway leaf rubbed over a joint of beef before cooking will impart a 'noble' flavour. For a vegetable dish Caraway

leaves improve the taste of such leaves as the highly beneficial Comfrey and of other herbs—and they are particularly
good to cook with cabbage, cauliflower and similar vegetables to which they contribute a piquant flavour and help
their digestibility. And for these purposes a teaspoonful of
Caraway seeds in a muslin bag should be boiled with these
green vegetables, they will also lessen the unpleasant smell
of their cooking. The thick, tapering, young roots, cooked
like parsnips, make tasty eating.

Caraway seeds have various other uses; they are good to
eat with raw or baked apples; in fruit salads; to be mixed
inside and scattered over the top of a 'Seed Cake'; to be
mixed into bread, as they are in Scandinavian countries.
They are good blended into cheeses. Cordials and liqueurs
are made from Caraway, and the best known is the popular
'Kummel'.

Caraway's valuable constituents of various oils and
liquids, fats and protein, are aromatic, tonic and stimulant.
They relieve the stomach of digestive difficulties and flatulence, and they soothe nervous hysteria. Caraway leaves or
seeds should go into the tea infusions.

And, according to ancient belief, Caraway seeds were put
into 'love potions' to hold lovers and prevent their straying!

CHAMOMILE   *Anthemis nobilis*

The Chamomile is primarily a medicinal herb of such general benevolence that, it is said, if a Chamomile plant is set

near any sickly plant in a garden it will aid its recovery.

The whole plant when fresh is aromatic, smelling of apples, and the Spaniards call it 'Manzanilla', a little apple, and give this name to one of their light Sherries which is flavoured with Chamomile. The plant is greyish-green in colour and downy, and its scent gives no hint of its bitterish taste. The double flowers are used medicinally, as they contain the qualities for treating the ailments for which the plant has long been employed. Their action is tonic; soothing to upset stomachs; they allay nervous pains and relieve flatulence, and are taken in the form of a tea infused from 1 oz of the flowers to 1 pint of boiling water. This, like all herb teas, should be made in a covered vessel to prevent the steam escaping with the virtuous properties. This infusion should stand ten minutes before being strained. A wineglassful of the cool tea taken at bedtime is an old-fashioned but extremely effective remedy for nervous debilities. It is sedative and soothing and ensures quiet, peaceful sleep without nightmares. The flower tea is also effective in dropsical complaints, such as swollen ankles. It relieves colic, liver upsets and loss of appetite. Many people take a regular nightcap of Chamomile tea made with seven dried flowers to a breakfastcupful of boiling water, or five flowers to a teacupful.

Chamomile fomentations for external swellings, neuralgia or abscesses are made with muslin bags loosely stuffed with flowers and steeped well in boiling water before being applied. Chamomile is antiseptic and quite a safe remedy for any of the complaints I have given.

As a garden subject, Chamomile plants make bushy little subjects for the herb bed, and only the double flowers should be used in the tea, the single ones, which often occur, are injuriously strong. A plushy Chamomile lawn, or a path, is a great pleasure, and 'the more it is trodden, the more it will spread'. It likes a light sandy soil.

The dried flowers are stocked by all good herb shops.

CHERVIL   *Anthriscus cerefolium*

Chervil is one of the most important of flavouring herbs, but it has never had a medicinal reputation beyond its being soothing and warming for chilled stomachs. Continental cooks use it daily to flavour many dishes, and no French herb bouquet, 'Fine Herbes', would be complete without its fern-like leaves. The plant is an annual growing up to 18 inches high, resembling a small Sweet Cicely, with bright green finely cut foliage which fades to a purplish-pink colour (pretty foliage for flower arrangements). The tiny blossoms are borne in umbels, like Sweet Cicely's.

Chervil has a rich individual flavour—sometimes likened to caraway, but I think that is stretching the imagination a little—which blends well with any meat dish, casserole or stew, and with most fish dishes. The finely chopped leaves are good sprinkled in salads, or used as a garnish as parsley is used. Chervil makes a tasty herb vinegar for dressings, also a delicious herb butter. Finely chopped, it is an asset mixed into the mayonnaise to be served with cold asparagus; it goes well into any soup, especially chicken soup. And the French make several soups based on this herb.

Chervil is easy to cultivate, it is an annual, but the seeds are generously sown from the plants, so that after the first planting it will come up year after year. As the seeds rapidly lose their germinating power, bought seed is often disappointing, and it is better to buy some small plantlets from a herb nursery to start the garden supply. Given fairly rich moisture-holding soil in a little shade, Chervil should be available through most of the year, even during winter.

Dried Chervil may be bought from herb stores.

CHICKWEED   *Stellaria media*

The succulent little Chickweed creeps into every garden; usually unwelcomed and ousted by the gardeners—unless they let it rip as a harmless annual surface-rooting weed that acts well as a mulch for their precious summer crops. Actually, chickweed should be regarded in its own right as a crop of nourishing cress. This plant has a high, and ancient, reputation among herbalists, who appreciate its true worth as a soothing and curative herb from which they make very effective ointments and other medications.

Chickweed is one of the few edible plants which amass a rich content of copper. The virtuous edible kind of garden bed and border—and of newly ploughed fields—must not be confused with the aptly named Mouse-ear Chickweed which sits tightly in lawns, spreading small, dark green, rather whiskered leaves. The real cress Chickweed is a weak-looking plant with much-branched, pale translucent stems and bright green, pointed oval smooth leaves borne in pairs; and it produces tiny white flowers with narrow petals like the rays from a star.

As a culinary herb, fresh Chickweed is a good salad cress, tender and cool. When cooked as a vegetable, it is like the most tender and delicate of spring spinach, and even more wholesome—but a good deal is needed for this dish, as it shrinks in the boiling. As a cress for sandwiches, Chickweed goes well with anything, tomato, cheese, egg, cucumber: and deliciously appetising sandwiches are made from thin brown bread and butter, with a few drops of Worcester sauce, Chickweed cress and shredded Dandelion leaves. However it is used, Chickweeds offers its valuable constituents for our own needs.

Medicinally, Chickweed is soothing and it reduces inflammation. The fresh leaves make an effective poultice for any inflamed part of the body, even the eyes; also, such an application will relieve ulcers and effectively cope with boils, carbuncles and external abscesses and piles. To make such a poultice, place the Chickweed in a muslin bag and boil it in a little water for two or three minutes; then apply the bag poultice to the affected place—and use the water to bathe the part.

The tea made from Chickweed—freshly gathered or dried—is mildly laxative; comforting to weak digestions;

good against scurvy and skin ailments. It makes an excellent lotion to bathe tired inflamed eyes, or to bathe skin eruptions—and it has long been drunk as a slimming herb (infuse a loose handful of the fresh herb, or a teaspoonful of the dried, to a pint of boiling water). Chickweed is also an old and tried remedy for chilblains—either the ointment bought from a herbalist or the one which can be made at home. For this, use an old saucepan and boil a mass of chickweed until it is reduced to a thick green pulp; then add some pure lard, mix well and put into a clean pot. This does not keep very long.

The dried herb is obtainable from herb stores.

CHIVES   *Allium schoenoprasum*

This is a herb which should be in every garden or window box; it has the most delicate of onion flavours, and is much to be preferred to its stronger relations for many dishes, where the big onion's taste is too harsh and pervading. The Chive is a gregarious little plant, and so quickly multiplies into a dense cluster of bulbs that it is usually referred to in the plural. Only the bright green hollow, grass-like leaves are used, and these should be taken from several plants and cut close to the ground so that the bulbs are not entirely scalped and will quickly throw up new growth; and they must not be allowed to produce their pretty clusters of mauve flowers, or the quality of their precious leaves will deteriorate.

Chives have much the same health-giving qualities as all the onion types, the pungent volatile oil and a rich content of sulphur, which gives them their onion-like flavour and is antiseptic. They encourage the appetite and comfort the stomach by aiding the digestion. Their mild oniony flavour goes well with any savoury dish. Chives make the ideal garnish for a grilled steak—when chopped fine and mixed with butter—Chive butter is good, too, spread on the toast under a Welsh rarebit, or scrambled eggs, or grilled tomatoes. Chives are the zest of any salad, casserole or stew, stuffings, meat balls and savoury omelettes, and mashed or creamed potatoes. A complete list of their uses would fill a cookery book. But I cannot imagine what I should do without my Chives. If I lived in a town flat I should grow them in a window box or a plant pot on the kitchen window-sill.

Chives grow about 8 inches high. They like a good rich, light soil, and the garden clumps should be lifted and divided every two years, then replanted in bunches of about nine little bulbs, setting the bunches 6 inches apart.

CICELY   *Myrrhis odorata*

Sweet Cicely is a lovely culinary herb with lacy fern-like leaves, often flecked with patches of white as though with icing-sugar; and frothy umbles of white flowers. An old herbalist describes this plant as 'so harmless you cannot use it amiss'. For its appearance and for its uses it should be given a place in every garden. The whole plant is aromatic, smelling rather like aniseed, and it has the virtue of being good for the heart, the stomach and the bronchials, so that it relieves flatulence, palpitations, coughs and catarrh. It helps the liver and is in the treatment for pleurisy and anaemia, and is said to be especially good for young girls. The tea used for these specific ailments may be infused from the fresh or dried leaves, or a decoction of the dried root, which is put into cold water and boiled—at the rate of 1 oz to $1\frac{1}{2}$ pints, boiled until reduced to 1 pint. And a large leaf can be included in the daily blending of herb tea.

As a culinary herb, the leaves give a rich but indescribable flavour to casseroles or stews, and to soups. The fresh roots are tasty chopped into salads, and, as the plant seeds very freely in a garden, the small crisp roots of the unwanted plants also make a good addition to salads. Fair-sized roots well boiled and eaten with oil and vinegar dressing are good. And the inch-long young green seeds, while crisp and juicy, are delicious as a little side-salad, also dressed with oil and vinegar. The ripe seeds, hard and brown, should be kept for flavouring winter stews and other dishes—these should be bruised before use. On the Continent these seeds are ground up like pepper into a flavorous condiment.

Sweet Cicely may be safely enjoyed by diabetics, and it provides an excellent stimulant for elderly people and for the young.

This is a hardy perennial plant which prefers a shady site

in a dampish bed, where it will grow large and be a splendid foliage plant in a dull corner.

CLOVER   *Trifolium pratense*

Red Clover, Clover-rose, Sugar-bosses, does not creep over the ground as White Clover spreads; it may grow up to 2 feet tall with several lax stems carrying the well-known 'lucky' three leaflets, and if they sport four leaflets these are considered to be much more potent charms. But Clover has other more practical virtues. The plant builds up mineral stores which are beneficial for our several purposes: the sodium it contains reduces acidity and helps the body to assimilate iron, a process which is difficult for some people to achieve naturally, so that they tend to become anaemic. For such assistance, Clover is an excellent herb to accompany the iron-giving plants such as Nettle, Dandelion and Sweet Cicely in the daily remedial herb teas.

Clover aids the kidneys, and its frequent use prevents catarrhs, or if catarrh is suffered this is one of the best herbs with which to treat it. Both the rose-pink flowers and the leaves make an effective tea for relieving bronchial coughs. And Clover tea has an ancient well-deserved reputation for easing the strain of whooping-cough. For this purpose the tea is even more effective when Clover, Mallow and Thyme are mixed for its making and Garlic pills are taken.

This herb has the virtue of healing damaged tissues, so that they may resume their natural functions. And it prevents or cures cramp spasms.

The curative tea can be infused from the fresh plant, leaves and flowers, or from the dried parts stocked by herbalists. To make it, pour a pint of boiling water over 1 oz of the herb—cover and drink when cool in wineglassful doses several times daily.

White Clover has a talent for warding off mumps, and when such an epidemic threatens a community Clover honey is a useful precaution, and as this particular honey contains other Clover virtues, I recommend its use as a sweetener for any of the herb teas.

Both the pink- and the white-flowered Clovers make a very pleasurable wine, and it is worth finding a Clover field that will provide the necessary gallon of bloom-heads.

COLTSFOOT   *Tussilago farfara*

Coltsfoot, Foalsfoot or Coughweed, as it is popularly called for its service to mankind, is a common weed where the ground is poorly cultivated; on railway embankments, waste places and in gardens; in soils wet or dry Coltsfoot will flourish. The long white creeping roots throw up pretty bright yellow, daisy-like flowers in spring, and as they disappear, up comes the dense foliage, the scalloped heart-shaped, sea-green leaves. This plant was so esteemed by the herbalists that they long ago adopted the flowers as their sign to be painted on the doorposts of their shops. All parts of the herb have uses: the leaves and flower-stalks are especially effective for the treatment of coughs, bronchial catarrh and asthma, and while their virtues soothe, they heal the 'tubes' and organs affected, and they will loosen phlegm, so that even the hardest cough is eased by the use of Coltsfoot in some form, the cough mixture, the cough candy or the Coltsfoot Rock. The smoking of the British herb tobacco, for which Coltsfoot is the basic ingredient, gives relief to sufferers from bronchial obstructions which make breathing difficult.

A certain relief from wheezing, dry coughs, asthma and colds is promised by a decoction of Coltsfoot leaves—alone or with Marsh Mallow. This is made with 1 oz of the dried leaves in a quart of water and boiled down to a pint, then sweetened with honey. It should be taken frequently in tea-cupful doses.

Coltsfoot tea, infused with or without Marsh Mallow, answers much the same purpose as the decoction, and is taken in the same dosage. It is made by pouring 1 pint of boiling water over 1 oz of the dried herb, and may with advantage be sweetened with honey. The vessel must be covered to trap the virtuous steam when making all decoctions and infusions.

Dried Coltsfoot leaves can be bought from any good herbal store or they may be used freshly gathered.

Coltsfoot flowers make a good tonic wine.

COMFREY, COMMON
RUSSIAN COMFREY

Symphytum officinale
Symphytum peregrinum

Comfrey, Knit-bone, has sustained its ancient standing as one of the most valuable of all herbs, with the power to relieve and to cure various difficult ailments. Among this plant's constituents there is an unusual abundance of mucilage, which can sooth and heal internal organs and external wounds or sores: some iodine is present, with salts, tannin, sugar, also a high count of protein, some potash and, as its peculiar virtue, there is Allantoin, which acts like magic in all deficiency diseases, for which it is aided by a vitamin B 12 content—this is rare in vegetables, and is contained in pig's liver for patients suffering from pernicious anaemia and other blood complaints.

In addition to these virtues, Comfrey is well equipped to help in the treatment of pulmonary and bronchial ailments, asthma, catarrh, whooping-cough and quinsy; it will deal with boils, carbuncles and the obstinate spots which are often distressing for adolescents; it provides a wonderful treatment for stubborn external ulcers, and for duodenal ulcers. With its astringency and soothing mucilage, Comfrey supplies a gentle remedy for diarrhoea or dysentery. And in some cases it banishes the pain of arthritis.

For such complaints a decoction of the root is recommended to be made by boiling 1 oz of crushed root, fresh or dried, in 1 quart of water or milk, until the liquid is reduced to $1\frac{1}{2}$ pints, this should be taken frequently·in wineglassful doses. And it is also of great assistance for staunching internal bleeding and especially for the relief of bleeding piles. The patient should persist with the decoction until the bleeding ceases.

Comfrey tea is infused by pouring 1 pint of boiling water on 1 oz of leaves—dried, or if fresh, stripped from midrib—and it must be covered to preserve the steam. This tea is taken frequently in wineglassful doses to cope with the diseases for which Comfrey is the suitable treatment. The tea also acts as a general tonic, a blood purifier and a regular health insurance.

The leaves, dried or fresh, stripped from midrib, make exceedingly effective poultices and fomentations. They are chopped up and mixed with a little boiling water, then the mass is sandwiched between two pieces of gauze. These applications will reduce any inflammatory swelling, sprains, bruises, severe cuts, boils, abscesses, carbuncles or ulcers. And—for which accomplishment Comfrey was named Knit-bone—they will greatly assist the healing of broken bones.

Comfrey medications are available ready for easy use—there is Comfrey ointment, which is one of the safest and most efficient remedies to keep handy, for cuts, bruises and burns; and it has been known to work wonders in cases of eczema, ulcers, piles, spots, dermatitis—even corns: this external cream treatment is helped in its work if it is accompanied by a course of Comfrey tea, or tablets.

Comfrey tablets provide an easy way to benefit from the

herb, and a Comfrey tea is sold to brew as, or with, an ordinary tea. There is also a finely powdered condiment made to be shaken pepper-like over food, or to be put into soups, stews, broths or gravies.

Although Comfrey's benefits are secured by these convenient items, other uses of the herb can be enjoyed when it is grown in the garden. Comfrey is a large, handsome plant, but an invasive one that should be given a place where it can increase without affecting other less arrogant subjects. The Russian Comfrey is a good type to plant; it grows up to 4 feet tall, with thick bristly branching stems and hairy sea-green leaves of various sizes. The delightful purple-blue trumpet flowers are borne along drooping, curved heads on the ends of the branches, and they bloom from early spring until late autumn. The plant is not fussy about soil so long as it is not poor and too dry in summer, and it will gladly furnish a rather shady site.

Comfrey supplies fresh young leaves for a wholesome and very nutritious, high-protein, vegetable dish. For this, choose tender leaves, cut out the midrib and after washing them place them dripping wet into a saucepan with only a tablespoonful of water. Cook gently and keep turning the leaves to avoid burning. When cooked and strained, chop up the leaf mass with butter or margarine, season with pepper, a dash of nutmeg and squeeze over a little lemon juice. Without these additions I find cooked herbs rather insipid, and I like to add either chopped Chives, Garlic or Spring Onion.

Comfrey would be worth growing if only for the pleasure of the delicious, crisp fritters made from it. For these, mix the special batter I have given for Elderflower fritters and dip in young Comfrey leaves and fry them in hot oil or fat, serve hot with castor sugar sprinkled over.

COUCH-GRASS   *Agropyron repens*

Couch-grass, Twitch-grass, Dog-grass, produces a coarse green grass on top and a thick mat of creeping roots underneath. It is the gardeners' despair, unless they suffer bladder complaints or some other ills, then it can be their comfort. As Dog-grass, dogs and cats, who instinctively know their natural medicines, seek for this herb if they are poorly; and if it is available they will eat it regularly to keep fit and healthy.

Couch-grass is one of the most important of medicinal herbs for relieving such bladder and kidney complaints as nephritis (inflammation of the kidneys), and especially cystitis, and it will relieve any other upset which causes painful urination, as for example, gravel. It is also employed in the treatment of gout and of rheumatism, and for promoting perspiration to relieve feverish conditions. In France and other continental countries the herb's roots are made into a popular domestic tisane to be taken not only for curative purposes but also as a spring-time 'cleanser' and a safeguard against the ills for which it is known to be effective. And it will provide certain mineral nutrients which are necessary for health and are not always available in ordinary foods.

The most valuable constituents in Couch-grass are the rich supplies of potassium, chlorine, silica and other desirable elements, including a special carbohydrate, and a highly beneficial sugar which is held to be the herb's particularly potent weapon for comforting the kidney and bladder diseases for which it is famed.

To make the tea, or tisane, infuse 1 oz of the cleaned whisker-free roots cut into short pieces, with 1 pint of boiling water. The roots can be fresh from the garden or bought dried from a good herbal store. The infusion is sweet, but otherwise tasteless, and I usually add a flavouring of honey and lemon juice or some other herb such as parsley or fennel. The tea should be taken freely in wineglassful doses. A regular course of this treatment is recommended by herbalists as a safe and easy cure for cystitis.

COWSLIP   *Primula veris*

Once upon a time the sweetly scented Cowslip flowers could be gathered in quantities sufficient to provide many highly enjoyable and beneficial things. But today the lush Cowslip-speckled meadows are fast disappearing and leaving us the poorer for their loss. Not only do we lack Cowslip pleasures, the deliciously scented, drooping Fairy Cups—as they were called—with their ruby spot at the base of each petal, but we are bereft of the most delicious of country wines, and of the blossom conserve, the blossoms on salads

46

and the delightful Cowslip tea. Fortunately this can still be made from the dried flowers available as Cowslip tisane which will relieve insomnia and other ills; and make the lotion so widely used to beautify ladies in past centuries. Then, village children brought baskets of Cowslips to sell to the great houses, where, in the still-rooms, the yellow petals were converted into delicious commodities for the dining- and the dressing-tables.

Cowslip's constituents are sedative and antispasmodic. The tea, the tisane, is infused from a handful of the fresh yellow corollas pinched out of their green calyxes—or two teaspoonfuls of dried flowers—to 1 pint of boiling water. This will provide comfort for a lot of our present-day problems. For its sedative qualities it can be enjoyed during the day and at bedtime, when it will induce sweet peaceful sleep; and it will cope with giddiness from nervous strain, or over-excitement. It relieves muscular rheumatism and is an effective soother of cramps and spasms—even paralysis— for which the plant was called Palsywort. And it is reputed to strengthen the memory.

This same infusion makes an excellent lotion for clearing the skin of blemishes and sunburn, and preventing wrinkles.

For Cowslip conserve, pound the fresh blossoms to a pulp in a mortar; weigh the mass, and to every ounce add 3 oz of honey or castor sugar. Then beat the mixture until it is thoroughly blended before potting in little pots and sealing. Flower conserves are delicious and beneficial, and may be eaten with a teaspoon as sweetmeats.

DANDELION

Taraxacum officinale

The Dandelion is one of my favourite herbs, and I am sure its qualities should be more widely known and exploited. The 'weed' was not always so neglected in Britain as it is today. Not a hundred years ago it was planted—and ·deliberately—in the best kitchen gardens, to be tended and nurtured with the best manure, so that its resulting great fat tender leaves could be served at table to princes, parsons or plebeians. It is still, deservedly, treated so in France, where it is cultivated for market and served in the best restaurants. This golden-disc-flowered herb's excellent virtues are available for ordinary culinary uses and for medications. It has a very high vitamin A content; four times more vitamin C than lettuce; much more iron than spinach; and a rich content of potassium is also stored within its green leaves and fang-like roots, along with other, valuable constituents. The flowers, too, have their share of good things to offer, as well as their nectar, for our salads. As this plant's principal curative effects act on the liver, the kidneys, the bladder, the heart and the stomach, it can only be a beneficial addition to any diet, and the best ways to use it are in salads, as a vegetable, as a substitute for real coffee and especially in the herb teas taken daily.

IN SALADS use several of the tenderest leaves (not too many) with lettuce and other saladings. They give a nice bitterish flavour which is rather like chicory, and add some of the bright golden flowers which have a delicate tangy flavour.

AS A VEGETABLE, use alone or with nettles or spinach, or any other leaf vegetable, about half and half. Wash the leaves and put them dripping wet into a pan with a piece of butter or margarine—the size depends on the amount of leaves—boil gently and keep turning so that they do not burn and the butter becomes well mixed with the greenery. When half cooked add the young nettle tops (which cook quicker) washed, and with the thickest stalks removed. Keep turning until cooked, then strain—keep the juice to mix into any soup—add a garnish of chopped Chives or Spring Onion, more butter if necessary, and a squeeze of lemon juice, season with salt and pepper. When chopped up this also makes a good base for poached eggs to sit on.

Dandelion's curative powers may have given it its French name—*Dent de lion,* from which Dandelion is a corruption. In the fifteenth century it was reported that 'the herb was much employed by Master Wilhemus, a surgeon who, on account of its virtues, likened it to a lion's tooth'. I am not very happy about the virtues of a lion's tooth, but I am confident of those of the Dandelion. A few leaves included in one's daily half-pint of herb tea have a noticeable effect on the digestion, and anyone who is troubled with flatulence, heart-burn, perhaps unable to digest fats, will find that Dandelion leaves—with other herbs such as Sweet Cicely, Balm, Fennel, infused into the herb tea—will offer relief or, if taken daily, will remove the trouble. The plant's power over the liver and stomach is extraordinarily rapid, and kidney and bladder troubles seem to be quickly relieved by the tea; but it must be remembered that Dandelion leaves are most efficient when used with other herbs. The rich iron content of the leaves is some insurance against anaemia and scurvy, which seem to affect quite a number of people. The Dandelion is slightly aperient; also it was once considered to be an effective herb for preventing and for relieving gravel. It is effective, too, for clearing the complexion and for skin eruptions and disorders. I have also heard of its dissolving the chalky deposits which are a symptom of rheumatoid arthritis.

As a recommended herbal treatment for eczema and scurvy, a tea is made by boiling 2 oz of Dandelion root, or the leaves, in 1 quart of water until it is reduced to 1 pint. This infusion should be taken in wineglassful doses every 3 hours. If Ground Elder, Goutweed, is available, add 1 oz of the fresh leaves to this brew.

Dandelion coffee, as a substitute for the real coffee, may be drunk by children or invalids at bedtime or any time. It does not contain the excitant caffeine and actually induces peaceful sleep. This can be bought ready made. To make it at home, dig up the roots of two-year-old plants in autumn when they are well stored with food reserves, cut off the crowns, wash away the soil, and dry them first with a cloth, then in a cool oven. They may be stored for a few months in an air-tight tin in a dry place. As required, roast them to a light brown colour and grind them as coffee.

Dandelion beer is a good refreshing drink, and wine made from the flower petals can resemble fine light sherry.

'Dill that hindereth witches of their will' is an ancient magician's herb, and one of the oldest medicinal plants to be recorded, as it was found to be in an Egyptian list of 5,000 years ago. Dill must therefore have thwarted a great many witches and comforted a vast number of people from the cradle to the grave, quietening hiccoughs and curing flatulence, and giving sound peaceful sleep to the restless.

Dill is a favourite culinary herb on the Continent, where the fresh plant and the seeds have many uses. The leaves or seeds add a spicy flavour to stews, casseroles and soups, and French confectioners put the seeds into cakes and pastries. This herb is right for fish dishes, or fish soup and potato soup. It partners Tarragon in sauce for asparagus, and Parsley in cream sauce for artichokes, and it is good sprinkled on raw cucumber. The Scandinavians use Dill leaves as the British use Mint, added to and sprinkled over new potatoes and peas.

Dill seeds soaked in white malt or wine vinegar for a week make a tasty, aromatic vinegar to blend into the salad dressing, or to use on cucumber, sardines or tinned herrings and pilchards. And the fresh leaves may be cooked with fish.

Dill is the well-known herb used when pickling cucumbers, gherkins and cauliflowers. The fresh leaves are laid beneath each layer of cucumber and the seeds are sprinkled over the top. Dill's constituents, the various oils, are almost identical with Caraway's, and there is very little to choose between Dill and Fennel for culinary purposes.

Medicinally, Dill has considerable virtues as an aid to the digestion, a soother of upset stomachs, and it has some reputation among herbalists as a stimulant for the brain. Either a few leaves or half a teaspoonful of the seeds should be mixed with the herbs in tea infusions made for regular drinking. Tea infused from Dill seeds—a teapoonful to half a pint of water—relieves flatulence and stomach upsets.

For the garden, Dill is an annual plant to grow from seed sown in spring in any good soil. It closely resembles Fennel in appearance, but it is a much smaller plant, producing one main stem, whereas Fennel is a branching plant.

Bunches of fresh Dill can be bought at certain times of the year from good greengrocery stores, and Dill seeds are available at any time from any health food shop. There are several medications on the market which contain Dill oil.

ELDER   *Sambucus nigra*

The Elder or Elderberry tree is so familiar that it needs no description. I am sure everybody knows its bright green leaves and flat masses of tiny cream-coloured scented flowers in early summer; followed later by drooping bunches of black-purple juicy berries.

Every part of this common small tree is valuable—even the young green stems, which make an excellent pickle. The bark, the leaves, the flowers and berries all have their uses, domestic, culinary and medicinal, as the tree has many virtues and is a great healer. The chemical constituents are impressive enough for its parts to be widely used in herbal remedies and sold for various disorders and healing ointments. It also provides very desirable cosmetic creams and toilet waters.

Elder's pleasurable culinary uses should be better known; the flowers have a muscat, grape-like flavour, and they make a really delightful white wine for maturing, and a quickly fermented fizzy 'Champagne'. The flower-heads make delicious fritters, for these, make this special batter—allow 1 oz of melted butter or good margarine, to 6 oz of flour, a pinch of salt and the yolk of an egg. Mix with a wooden spoon, adding at intervals a teacupful of tepid water. When creamy, let the batter stand for at least an hour, until wanted, then when ready to use, fold in the firmly beaten egg white. Dip the flat flower heads into the batter and put them into a waiting frying-pan with cooking oil already sizzling hot. Serve sprinkled with castor sugar.

The fresh flowers stripped of stalks when beaten into a good bun mixture give it their delicate flavour and make the batter light and fluffy.

As a domestic medicine, make an infusion with 1 oz of Elder flowers, fresh or dried, and 1 pint of boiling water. This must be kept covered to trap the steam. Taken in wineglassful doses several times during the day, this tea will relieve pleurisy, bronchial and pulmonary affections, measles and other eruptive diseases, such as scarlet fever. And it is an excellent and pleasant springtime pick-me-up for purifying the blood, the kidneys and the bladder if it is taken for several weeks in the mornings before breakfast. For a quick relief from influenza, make a strong infusion of a handful of dried Elder flowers and of dried Peppermint with 1½ pints of boiling water. Allow the jug to stand (covered) in a pan of hot water for half an hour, then strain, add a little honey and drink it as hot as is bearable in bed. This will ensure a heavy perspiration and a deep sleep, and if taken at the beginning of an attack it will very soon work a cure.

The weaker infusion of Elder flower tea, when cold, is an excellent lotion for bathing inflamed eyes, and also for the complexion.

Muslin bags stuffed with the dried flowers are recommended for use in the bath to relieve sciatica, rheumatism and skin troubles.

Elderberries make a rich red wine that is not only a pleasant tipple but is also curative and will guard against winter colds and chills. The cordial is effective too, and either brews—taken hot at night in the early stages of an attack—will cope with influenza, catarrhs, shivering colds and sore throats.

Ripe elderberries are tasty in apple pies, and they make an excellent jam or jelly—resembling Blackberry. They add their virtues to soup, broth, chutney and ketchup.

The leaves are employed in many of the herbal medications which are sold for specific diseases.

I have heard of Elder leaves' prowess in curing eczema.

For this treatment the fresh leaves were mashed up and the thick green juice was applied to the sores several times a day. By the end of three weeks the ailment had vanished.

FENNEL   *Foeniculum vulgare*

Fennel is a decorative aromatic plant that will enhance any garden; with leaves so fine and feathery that the plant resembles a 6-foot-high green fountain. The old herbalists credited the plant with being of great benefit to the eyes; and of reducing unwanted fat. And the old-time physicians were often right, for Fennel has been proved to have these effects in some degree. Its medicinal action is so entirely soothing and helpful that it is an ingredient in infants' Gripe Water, and is a part of Compound Liquorice Powder. The bruised seeds are the parts used in medicinal preparations and for teas—allowing one teaspoonful of bruised seeds to $\frac{1}{2}$ pint boiling water—but the leaves fresh from the garden plant make a good herb tea with certain helpful effects not only for 'weight watchers' but for general well-being; and the same brew provides a refreshing and toning lotion for the complexion. Fennel's several constituents, the oils and acids, which dispel flatulence and help the digestion to cope with fatty foods make it the proper accompaniment of salmon to correct this fish's oily indigestibility. This also applies to herrings and other fish with an oil content which affects many people. Fennel's flavour is especially good with many fish dishes, and should be tried in the sauce served with such fish as hake, cod and mackerel. The coarsely chopped herb should be added to a good white sauce, which should not be allowed to boil after the Fennel is put in.

Fennel's other uses are in salads, with cucumber, and in a fish salad. I have used the fresh Fennel leaves in place of Dill when pickling small cucumbers. The seeds are used in cakes and bread by continental cooks—and the peeled, tender stems, cut before flowering, are a popular Italian salad served with an oil, vinegar and pepper dressing.

Fennel is easy to grow in any good soil in a sunny or partially shaded position. The seeds can be bought, and they should be saved from garden plants for winter use.

GARLIC   *Allium sativum*

Garlic is a herb of great importance, beloved by cooks and by physicians. As a flavouring herb, used with discretion, it is worthy of almost any savoury dish, and too well known for my cookery comments, except that for casseroles and stews I find the flavour of whole, unbruised cloves of garlic nutty and subtle compared with the taste of the chopped cloves or expressed juice. And I must mention Garlic vinegar, which is made by placing about 2 oz of skinned and chopped cloves in a pint of white vinegar. This is delicious added to salad dressings.

But Garlic is not to be valued merely for its culinary uses, although its virtues are in some degree imparted to the food it flavours. Its medicinal qualities are many and valuable. It is antiseptic, and helps to resist infectious diseases. It is a stimulant and an aid to the digestion. It acts kindly on the kidneys and bladder; it helps to reduce hypertension and high blood pressure. In cases of bronchitis or bronchial catarrh garlic breaks up the phlegm obstructions and eases the coughing, and it is also of great comfort to patients suffering asthma and whooping cough. It has been known to alleviate dropsical conditions, and it relieves rheumatism. So it surely deserves to be enjoyed in food whenever possible.

In days gone by garlic preparations for the sickroom must have been hard to endure, for they were made from the pungent juice of the herb in mixtures suitable for their application as syrups, teas, poultices and greasy rubs! Nowadays we can benefit by the modern preparations in which the taste and smell are not evident. There are the pills, the perles and the garlic pearls with the wonderful juice tightly contained in a gelatine capsule, and the Garlic tablets, all to be swallowed and forgotten and unsuspected by one's closest companions. They will allow garlic to cope with the diseases it is capable of relieving. Also, they can be taken to resist infection in crowded places—or during epidemics.

There is a garlic ointment available that deals with cuts, bruises, stings and rheumatic pains.

GOOSE-GRASS, CLEAVERS   *Galium aparine*

This is a seriously intentioned annual herb in spite of its pet
names, such as Sticky Willie—which it deserves for its
sticking and clinging sprays of long angular, weak, rough
stems with whorls of narrow leaves, and its insignificant
flowers, which produce the fruits as round, green, burrs.
Every part of this plant is eager and equipped to attach itself
to any passing human or animal, with its hook-like hairs, its
'lover's knots', the seeds are thus spread far and wide for
next year's crop, which will envelop other plants and make
green-lit arbours over our garden flowers.

But herbalists and homeopaths like the 'weed' and exploit
its quite considerable virtues in remedies for various complaints; and it is also highly recommended to be included in
the herb teas infused for regular use. The whole plant,
except the root, makes a good tea when brewed like ordinary tea—and the burrs, dried and lightly roasted, are considered to be the best substitute for real coffee and have a
coffee flavour—which is not really surprising, as this herb is
related to the true coffee plant.

Cleavers' valuable constituents are chlorophyll, starch
and three particular acids—tannic, citric and rubichloric—
and their effects are to purify the blood and to combat liver
disorders, to induce peaceful sleep, to rectify many skin
complaints and relieve dropsical conditions, also gravel
deposits and bladder stone are relieved by their considerable
effect on urinary secretions and the urinary organs. Goose-

grass is also a valuable aid to the digestion and is an old-fashioned remedy for head colds and for obesity. The herb's astringent properties make it an effective treatment for diarrhoea and to staunch some bleeding.

The tea, made by infusing a good-sized bunch of Goosegrass tops or 1 oz of the dried herb with a pint·of boiling water, is a good household remedy for many of the ills I have mentioned and should be taken, hot or cold, in wineglassful doses several times a day.

This herb is also recommended for the treatment of psoriasis, eczema, scurvy, scrofula, acne and other skin maladies. In such cases the expressed juice is taken at the rate of 3 oz twice a day. Alternatively, put a bunch of the herb rolled round to the size of a bird's nest into a saucepan and just cover with water; boil for 20 minutes; then cool in a covered container. Drink a wineglassful two or three times a day.

This herb's powerful action on the kidneys makes it unsuitable for anyone with a tendency to diabetes.

GOUTWEED   *Aegopodium podagraria*

Goutweed, Ground Elder, is a naughty weed, but a benevolent herb. I cannot suggest that it should be deliberately grown in the garden, but if it is already there it should be used. And it is of such value that it is worthwhile asking gardeners who are pestered with the weed for some of its leaves.

This is a low-growing perennial plant reaching about $1\frac{1}{2}$–2 feet high, with bright green, rather large leaves, oval in shape and sharply toothed. They are carried on long stalks with a few stem leaves of varying sizes. The tiny white flowers are borne in umbels, carrot-like, and the ripe seeds pop and spin over the garden to ensure a fresh supply of plants, independent of the creeping roots.

As a vegetable Goutweed is the most spicy and tasty of the wholesome herbs. To cook it, wash the tender young leaves and put them dripping wet into a saucepan with a tablespoonful of water to prevent their burning, stir them around over a low heat. Strain when cooked and season with a little salt and pepper, chop in a knob of butter and serve hot.

As a curative herb, Goutweed's constituents make it particularly effective for treating several ailments. It is good for the kidneys and bladder, it is sedative, a cleanser of the internal organs, and an enemy of gout, sciatica, aching joints and of obstinate skin troubles such as eczema. For relieving these distresses an infusion made with a handful of the leaves to a pint of boiling water should be made fresh each day and taken in teacupful doses. In cases of gout, sciatica and aching joints, a hot fomentation of the leaves will ease the painfully inflamed parts to which it can be applied. But for eczema the fomentations must not be applied, the tea taken inwardly is sufficient to give relief. Goutweed, or Goutwort, pills are also effective, and can be bought from some herbal stores.

GROUND IVY   *Glechoma hederacea*

Ground Ivy, Gill-go-over-the-ground it was once called, when it was used to clear the brewing ale before hops were introduced. As a wild plant it is to be found almost everywhere in the countryside trailing its sprays of evergreen, rather hairy, heart-shaped scalloped leaves and tiny, lipped, blue-purple flowers. The whole plant is aromatic and tastes rather bitter because of the particular volatile oil it contains, and for this it is valued medicinally. It is an astringent, a stimulant, it acts with particular efficiency on the bladder and kidneys, and it is an old cure for digestive troubles. It is cooling for feverish bouts, it relieves coughs and pulmonary complaints. It is recommended in cases of jaundice, sciatica or gout. In fact, it was the all-purpose herb of past generations, and was taken to America by the early settlers.

This herb makes an excellent cooling and curative drink long known and used in the country as Gill tea, which is infused from 1 oz of the fresh or dried herb with 1 pint of boiling water, and sweetened with honey. When cool, this is taken several times a day in wineglassful doses. Gill tea is antiscorbutic and is a wholesome remedy for any of the ailments for which Ground Ivy is a suitable internal medication, especially for coughs and kidney diseases, for which the herb possesses a peculiar magic.

The same infusion is also of value as a lotion for bathing tired, inflamed, sore eyes.

As a highly efficient poultice for coping with gatherings,

abscesses and tumours, Ground Ivy should be combined with Yarrow or Chamomile flowers. The dried herb is available from good herb shops, and I recommend its inclusion in some of the herb teas infused for daily well-being.

GROUNDSEL   *Senecio vulgaris*

As Groundsel appears as a 'weed' in most gardens, we may as well know its virtues which recommend it to the herbalist, so that he collects it, dries it or expresses the juice from the fresh plant to make his potions. This herb's constituents make it a useful medicine for promoting perspiration when desirable. A strong brew is a purgative and a weak one a mild laxative, and it acts on the liver. It is a remedy for dispelling worms in children—or for anyone who may be affected. It is a safe emetic when one is necessary, and much more lenient than the usual mustard or salt dosages; and a mild infusion will relieve biliousness—one spray infused in a pint of water would be mild, two or three will make you comfortably sick—but with no unpleasant after-effects.

The herbal preparations which include Groundsel are made by herbalists with knowledge of its proportions and dosage. But the weed can serve several domestic purposes, and it makes a wonderfully soothing and healing lotion to bathe chapped hands. For this, infuse the fresh or dried plant and swab the roughness. A mild infusion—or tea—is especially soothing to bathe tired or inflamed eyes—and to relieve sunburn.

HAWTHORN   *Crataegus monogyna*

The Common Hawthorn, May Blossom, is a small thorny tree with a great reputation for its benefits: these have stretched from its being a protection for the home against lightning; a security for hope and domestic harmony; an emblem of sexual love to be used in the decorations for wedding ceremonies; to its place of importance in the apothecary's store, where it remains.

The short-stemmed simple leaves are deeply indented, and the fragrant blossoms of white or pink are borne in early summer in dense clusters at the end of leafy shoots. The fruits, the berries, the haws, turn red in autumn, and each one contains a single hard seed. When untrimmed the tree reaches a height of 30 feet.

All parts of Hawthorn have curative uses, and their constituents are astringent and stimulating. They act upon the bladder and kidneys to relieve any dropsical complaints, and they bring the tree high up in the list of curative herbs for the circulation of the blood. They have the power to dissolve deposits in the arteries and deal with arteriosclerosis and with any obstructions in the circulation, and are also a curative remedy for organic and functional diseases of the heart when there is enlargement, difficulty in breathing and rapid and feeble action. The Fluid Extract of Berries is available for the heart ailments, and is taken in doses of 10–15 drops as prescribed.

For a home-made infusion to keep the blood circulating

and the kidneys functioning healthily, 1 oz of the dried berries, leaves or flowers are infused with 1 pint of boiling water (kept covered), and this tea is taken in wineglassful doses several times during the day as a weekly insurance.

Both the fresh or dried flowers and berries make a useful decoction for curing a badly sore throat. For this, place a handful of the fresh flowers or berries—or 1 oz of dried—into 1½ pints of water and boil down to 1 pint, cover and use when cool.

For pleasurable uses Hawthorn leaves will improve a brew of ordinary tea—and add their virtues—and they may be brewed as a tea in their own right.

The berries will make a potent liquor; and with brandy and sugar, a good liqueur. And the blossoms make a delicious wine. A nice jelly can be made from the fresh berries.

The dried parts of Hawthorn are stocked by good herb shops.

HYSSOP   *Hyssopus officinalis*

This ancient sacred herb is a pleasurable plant for any garden, where it provides an aromatic, semi-evergreen shrub that is ordinarily about 2 feet high and wide; and in the warm western counties where it is often grown as a fragrant hedge plant, it achieves 3 or 4 feet. These hedges clip well into neat shapes, but by their cutting the delightful flower sprays are lost.

The fine odorous oils in the rich, dark green, narrow

leaves, and the small dark gentian-blue flowers, which are borne in whorls along the tips of the sprays, give a delightful scent—which I can only describe as a mixture of Russian leather and oil of lavender—and this makes the dried leaves and blossoms an excellent ingredient in pot pourri and sachets. And Hyssop is much used in the blending of choice liqueurs, especially in Chartreuse. The oil is also employed in the manufacture of good perfumes.

Hyssop's rich flavour merits its use as a potent culinary herb, and either fresh leaves and flowers from the garden or dried from the herb store should be put into soups, stews or any meat dishes, rich stuffings and sausages. Their flavour is strong, so that only a few leaves are necessary or desirable. A light sprinkling of minced or powdered leaves is good on salads—also the edible flowers.

This herb's constituents, the oils, resin, tannin, fats and other principles, make it a useful remedy for several disorders. It is recommended as a soother of wind and flatulence. It promotes perspiration when necessary at the start of a cold or chill. It relieves coughs and lung troubles, bronchial catarrh and asthma, and will clear upset stomachs. For the relief of all such ailments the stimulating and pleasant tea is infused from a good teaspoonful of the dried herb, or three or five small leafy or flowering tips from the growing plant, to 1 pint of boiling water, with a little honey added to sweeten. This should be taken in wineglassful doses three or four times a day. A few leaves should go every few days into the daily herb-tea mixture.

For external use a strong infusion of Hyssop leaves will ease the pain of muscular rheumatism and will quickly cure bruises. The bruised green leaves will heal cuts like magic.

Hyssop likes a bed of well-drained good light soil, in a sunny situation. It needs little attention apart from an occasional trimming back to avoid its becoming too lax and woody. There are also white- and pink-flowered Hyssops.

SEAWEED, KELP

I am using the name Seaweed as a general term for the various sea plants—Bladderwrack in particular—which are employed in modern herbal medications. The carefully dried Seaweed is called Kelp and appears under that name in the curative preparations sold in health food stores.

For the herbalist's purposes the Seaweed's harvesting is rather difficult and expensive, as the growing plants must be taken directly from the bed: once they are released, adrift or washed upon the shore disintegration quickly sets in, making the stuff only ideal as compost fertilisers for land plants to enjoy and assimilate Seaweed's riches for our benefit. Such is the value of Seaweed products in the garden.

It would be difficult to completely assess the value of Seaweed to man: it can contain all the basic elements by which all living things are maintained.

The earliest phase of the world was of barren basic rocks —granite—then molten into basalt, which over millions of years was changed and disintegrated to separate and release the minerals of its composition, some to mix and themselves be changed until life in tiny organic forms appeared and prospered in the muds. Then vegetation evolved which could assimilate the basic elements, and by its life cycle it returned to the rock sands, creating organic humus to support larger vegetation, and eventually animals, then man—both entirely dependent for their living upon the plants which alone could assimilate the raw materials provided by the rocks—and upon which all life has depended for its creation and development.

The continuous disintegration and the washing away by rain and wind of rock particles and mineral nutrients into rivers which transport their plunder into the seas—make the oceans the richly loaded sources of life's requirements. Seaweeds, living in the midst of this 'bank deposit', are equipped to take up the vital substances—some of which only the sea can provide.

From the products made from Seaweeds and seashore plants and from Kelp, we are assured of iodine, calcium, iron, with mineral nutrients and 'trace elements' as a bonus to the daily diet. Also by their stimulating the thyroid gland they serve for the special treatments of goitre and obesity; for healing tissues to bring them back to normal functioning; for guarding against, or relieving, scrofula; for remedying anaemia and all deficiency diseases, including those which are obvious by poor finger- and toe-nails.

The various types of preparations are sold by most health food stores. They range from powder to be sprinkled on food or put into soups and stews for a health-giving addition to ordinary food to pills or capsules for definite treatments.

LAVENDER
Lavandula officinalis

Lavender is among the best-known and most popular of aromatic herbs, but its virtues are now seldom exploited beyond its scent. This is much fancied in the bath, where it should not be regarded as just a pleasant smell when, in truth, the aroma is a stimulant. In the garden, where the beauty of the grey, evergreen, fragrant leaves and purple-blue flower spikes are enjoyed by the eyes and the nose, the little bush is rarely appreciated for its medicinal and culinary qualities.

The whole plant in late spring and summer is rich in a certain volatile oil composed of several constituents which are variously effective, and the complex is stimulating, wind dispelling and a restorative for nervous upsets or palpitations. It relieves faintness, spasms and colic, and it provokes the appetite. The essential oil or spirit of Lavender made from it is a useful and convenient medication to keep handy for such needs, when from one to four drops on a lump of sugar or taken in a little milk will prove comforting. But this concentrated essence can be dangerous if taken too frequently and in larger doses.

Lavender oil is good too, for external applications, for applying as a stimulant for paralysed limbs or cramps, as a cure for old sprains and stiff joints, or rheumatic pains. It is antiseptic and curative, and may be applied to mild burns, kitchen scalds, or to sores, bruises or insect bites.

A Lavender tea is infused from a teaspoonful of the flowers—fresh or dried—with 1 pint of boiling water—kept covered to trap the steam—if taken in occasional wineglassful doses it relieves flatulence and headache caused by exhaustion, fatigue or heat. And there is nothing more effective for restoring sore tired feet—and their exhausted owner—than a few drops of Lavender oil or a stronger infusion of the flowers in a warm foot-bath.

As a culinary herb, Lavender's flavour is pungent and slightly, but very agreeably, bitter. It does not 'perfume' food, but adds an enriching taste, plus an appetising smell. A sprig or two of the tender leaf-shoots in a casserole, stew or meat soup; a few leaves or a leafy spray laid on a roasting joint of lamb, will give delicious results and at the same time the herb will make the lamb more digestible.

For another pleasure a few tender Lavender leaves chopped up and added to a salad, with a light sprinkling of the flowers on top, make the dish appetisingly fragrant and give it a piquant flavour.

Conserve of Lavender flowers is an old-fashioned delicacy made by pounding the blossom 'pips' to a pulp, then adding three times its weight of solid honey and beating the mixture into a paste; then it should be potted in small screw-topped pots. This preserve was once placed on every elegant dining-table to be eaten sparingly, by little spoonfuls, as a condiment. Queen Elizabeth I was especially fond of it, and tasted it at almost every meal. This conserve goes well with those meat dishes which are usually accompanied with such preserves as red-currant jelly or mint jelly. For many centuries Lavender Conserve was also taken to relieve flatulence, nervous headaches, tensions and palpitations. And long ago small pillows stuffed with Lavender were used to induce sleep—and to discourage fleas, flies and other then common pests from their nightly attacks. Insects hate Lavender, and an occasional smear of the oil along the tops and corners of drawers or in wardrobes will keep moths away.

Lavender flowers should be harvested at the end of July or early August—on a dry, mild day—then the oil is at its best. And if the crop is good—or when the 'pips' can be bought—Lavender Vinegar is a possible luxury. It is made by filling a stoppered bottle with dried flowers and adding white or wine vinegar. The bottle must be shaken daily for a week, then the liquid is strained through fine muslin. The process may be repeated with fresh flowers if the perfume lacks strength. This toilet preparation is refreshing when dabbed on the temples. And it can be used to discourage midges or to treat their bites if they get there first.

Lavender grows well in a sunny position in any good garden soil that is not too acid. At least six plants should be available to supply flowers and leaves for a housewife's needs.

Where there is no garden space, a good health food store can supply the flowers, leaves and the oil, which is also sold by chemists.

LILY-OF-THE-VALLEY   *Convallaria majalis*

Lily-of-the-valley, Lily Constancy it was called, because the herb had a curative effect on the brain and strengthened memory, and it is still regarded by herbalists as one of the most important of the brain herbs. This is a lovely plant with its pairs of broad, oval, sharply pointed leaves sheathing the flower-stems, from which hang the bell-shaped, richly scented blossoms. It is better known today for the delightful perfume of the flowers than for the medicinal qualities for which it was once commonly valued. Actually, the perfume has a beneficial effect on the nerves, and was once distilled to provide a bedside remedial scent for nervous afflictions, although people's reactions vary to this as to other scents.

As an ancient medicinal herb, Lily-of-the-valley has not only retained its reputation but is becoming even more understood and appreciated, especially for its use in disease of the heart. It acts similarly to Digitalis, the Foxglove, but it is a little less powerful. It is a perfectly safe medication, and the precious constituents are soluble in water, so that the herb can be infused at home into an effective tea to remedy the complaints for which it is recommended, namely, cardiac, heart, kidney and bladder.

In severe cases of heart troubles Lily-of-the-valley in some form will probably be in the doctor's prescriptions, but the home-made infusion will be found very helpful for any patient suffering from a weak heart, and especially from the usual resulting dropsical condition. This herb tea slows down the disturbed action of the heart, but at the same time it increases the organ's strength. And it does not accumulate in the blood to cause any harmful side-effects. The infusion of $\frac{1}{2}$ oz of the dried herb to 1 pint of boiling water—kept covered—should be taken in tablespoonful doses several times a day, and when required to quieten palpitations. Half an ounce only must be infused, as a stronger brew will purge and cause vomiting.

The pleasurable uses of Lily-of-the-valley are the well-loved perfumes and the scented cosmetics. A deliciously scented oil can be made at home (if we have sufficient flowers). For this, fill a jar with fresh blossoms, add some oil of Sweet Almonds, or Olive Oil, press the flowers down so that their scent goes into the oil and let it stand for 24 hours. Then strain and press the oil from the mass—and add another lot of fresh blooms. The process must be repeated about a dozen times to produce the elegant bath oil to be lightly applied to dry parts of the skin; and it is a mildly effective, but highly pleasurable massage oil for easing little aches in the joints.

In Germany they used to make a wine from these flowers.

LIME TREE   *Tilia europae*

Lime, Linden or Tilleul, as the French call the tree, and the tisane they make from the flowers. This is their common domestic remedy for many ills and to make sure of a good night's sleep.

The tree may reach a height of well over a hundred feet, with rather sticky leaves that are heart-shaped and sharply toothed. When in flower with the lemony-white blossoms hanging from slender stalks in flattish clusters a Lime tree will headily scent the air around its neighbourhood and will hum with the sound of exultant bees. The rich nectar which drips from the flowers like fine sweet rain provides the best flavoured and most valuable of all the world's honeys, and this is almost exclusively used in medicines and is always chosen for the making of liqueurs.

Lime flowers not only contain a fragrant, volatile oil, tannin, sugar and gum but unlike most flowers they have chlorophyll in their make-up, which is usually confined to green leaves. This substance helps to cleanse the blood stream of poisonous deposits, it improves the state of the arteries and veins and considerably increases the efficacy of Lime-flower tea. This is infused by pouring 1 pint of boiling water on an eighth of an ounce of dried flowers—it is kept covered to retain the steam. The tea or tisane has a well-deserved reputation for relieving headaches, indigestion, hysteria and nervous upsets or palpitation. When taken hot, it will check diarrhoea caused by cold. Dried Lime blossoms should not be kept too long, as if the flowers used in the infusion are old and stale they may produce unpleasant symptoms.

Lime leaves and shoots are full of mucilage, and they make good poultices and fomentations.

Lime-wood charcoal is the first choice of many doctors for healing gastric ailments, and the powder is used for dressing burns and sores: it is finer and perhaps purer than the usual Willow charcoal.

Dried Lime flowers, or Lime-flower tisane, and Lime-blossom honey are stocked by most good herb stores.

LOVAGE   *Levisticum officinale*

Nowadays Lovage is one of the least known of the aromatic culinary herbs, yet it is an asset, both as a good-looking foliage plant and as a flavourous cooking herb, and I cannot understand why its popularity has declined from being, for many centuries, a familiar plant in most gardens, where it was grown for its food value and for its medicinal uses.

Lovage is a hardy perennial with erect, thick hollow stems 3 or 4 feet tall, with darkish-green leaves resembling those of a coarse-growing celery. The umbels of yellow flowers are followed by strongly aromatic seeds. All parts of the plant have a pungent odour and taste resembling celery with a little parsley in the background, so that the leaves, the stems or the seeds give a casserole, stew or soup this rich flavouring. In soups Lovage is good for chicken, meat and lentil. The chopped young leaves are nice in salads—especially in cabbage salad and one of raw vegetable. Wherever it is used, Lovage is entirely wholesome and beneficial, as well as delicious.

This herb's constituents, the oils, acids and resins, provide the plant's medicinal virtues. It relieves flatulence, reduces feverishness, it relieves colic—especially in children—it has a beneficial action on the kidneys and bladder and is recommended to ease menstrual pains. Added to all its virtues, Lovage is antiseptic enough to take the poison from a gnat bite if a piece of Lovage leaf is rubbed on the blister.

The tea may be infused from the fresh or dried leaves, or the seeds. Three whole leaves and stalks torn up—or a dessertspoonful of the dried, or a teaspoonful of the seeds, to a pint of boiling water. An infusion of the roots, fresh or dried, is preferred by some herbalists for the treatment of intestinal complaints and stomach disorders, also as a tea to be taken in cases of jaundice. But the leaf tea works well for ordinary upsets or as a health-giving tisane.

Lovage is easy to grow in a sunny bed of reasonably rich soil, and like most herbs, it gives its best flavour when treated to an annual dressing of compost.

The dried herb and seeds may be obtained from good health food shops or herbalists.

MARSH MALLOW   *Althaea officinalis*

The Mallows, with their greyish-green velvet leaves and soothing roots, with their pretty rose-mauve flowers, are entirely benevolent plants. They will adorn any garden and could provide handy medications. Their curative parts may be bought, dried, from a herb store, or made up into ointment and a soothing lotion for burns and pruritis, and into soap for rough or chapped skins. And there are also excellent cosmetic creams blended from Mallow. All these are important, because the Mallows contain wonderful gummy juices, curative oils and several other kindly elements which are exploited for their gentle, certain healing powers. They spread a coating like a soft emulsion over inflammations and irritations in such inaccessible places as the digestive organs, the urinary and respiratory tracts, and the intestines. A decoction that will relieve these distresses is made by boiling $\frac{1}{4}$ lb of dried root with 5 pints of water until the liquid is reduced to 3 pints: then it is strained. This is a boon to sufferers of painful ailments of the bladder, such as cystisis. It relaxes the tracts while having a curative effect on their soreness. This same decoction is used to cure bruises and sprains or aching muscles and sinews.

The powdered root boiled in milk is very effective for chest troubles, coughs, whooping cough and bronchitis, and it is a herbal treatment for dysentery.

Mallow's crushed fresh roots, or the powder, with slippery elm, make an effective poultice which can be a reliable cure for the most obstinate inflammations. This must be applied as hot as bearable, and the poultice should be renewed when dry. As Mallow prevents mortification in such cases, the plant was long ago named Mortification Root.

An infusion of 1 oz of the fresh or dried leaves to 1 pint of boiling water should be taken frequently in wineglassful doses for all the complaints mentioned; and the same infusion is excellent for bathing inflamed eyes.

In olden days, when food was what it claimed to be, the delicious 'Marsh Mallows' sold by confectioners were really made from the roots of this plant. And the downy leaves were enjoyed as a delicate vegetable dish, while the young tops and tender leaves were used in salads, as they are still eaten in France. The seeds, the round crisp 'cheeses', are good with a dressing of oil and vinegar. For these culinary purposes and for the herb's uses in the sick-room, rows of Mallows were cultivated in most gardens in sufficient quantity to supply leaves and roots to be used fresh or to be dried for store.

Nowadays, as the dried roots and leaves can be bought, this plant and its close relation, the Common Mallow, *Malva sylvestris*, with their attractive hollyhock-like blooms, are usually grown as pleasurable ornaments in the herb bed or border. Where, if necessary, they will conveniently supply a crushed leaf to quickly take away the pain and swelling of a wasp's sting.

Where these plants grow wild in the south of England and up to Lincolnshire, the young tender leaves should certainly be sought as a vegetable dish and cooked in the way I have explained for serving Nettles.

MARJORAM   *Oliganum*

Marjoram's strong scent and its flavour are often described as thyme-like, but I think this is misleading, the herb's warm, pungent savour is characteristic and cannot be obtained with any other herb. The taste and fragrance is retained when dried to increase its value as a culinary asset throughout the year. It was once much fancied as a bath scent, and for this purpose it is still used for its comforting action.

As a culinary herb, Marjoram imparts not only its flavour but also some of its curative virtues to food, making the dishes more easily digested and more appetising. Fresh from the garden or the grocer, or dried from a health food store, Marjoram goes into and improves a number of dishes such as soups, casseroles, stews, stuffings, omelettes, herb butters and cheeses; and salads, ordinary mixed ones, or those blended with raw vegetables. It is the correct herb to garnish special salads of Avocado Pear, or of water-cress and apple. Chopped or dried, Marjoram is a tasty garnish sprinkled over certain vegetables, Brussel sprouts, cabbage, cauliflower, carrots, mushrooms and marrows, and it is to be included in the mixture for a stuffed marrow. These flavorous sprays are important inclusions in a Bouquet Garni.

Marjoram tea infused from a handful of the fresh plant or a teaspoonful of the dried, with a pint of boiling water, relieves coughs and asthma; it comforts colic pains and quietens nervous hysteria, and headache, and palsy. The essential oil of Marjoram, which becomes a solid, is recommended for applying to stiff or paralytic limbs, for which distresses the tea also helps—and Marjoram bath-bags should be used in the bath for this treatment. And this bath herb will relieve stiffness, either from over-exertion or from rheumatism. The bath-bags are made by putting the herb— fresh or dried—into a muslin bag, a coarse weave for the fresh herb, organdie for the dried. They give a pleasurable scent to the bath water as they perform their curative tasks.

The most useful Marjorams for the garden are the low-growing perennial, Pot or French Marjoram, *Origanum onites*, which is quite hardy: and Sweet Marjoram, Knotted Marjoram, *O. marjorana*. This kind is only half-hardy, and must be grown in a cool greenhouse; as an old-fashioned pot-plant indoors; or as an annual, grown from seed sown under glass in March and planted out in June. The bed for these herbs should be reasonably sheltered and of dryish soil. They must not be water-logged in winter.

MINTS *Mentha*

The ancient Greeks discovered the Mint family's medicinal virtues, and we credit the Romans with the invention of mint sauce, which aids the digestion of such difficult immature meats as lamb. The common Mint, Lamb-mint, Spearmint, is so well known that I will not describe this particular type. Its culinary uses are legion and, as of old, it is used to flavour numerous dishes and sweetmeats. Both the Greeks and the Romans fancied the various Mints as bath per-fumes, and to rub and garland the tables laid for feasting, as 'The smell of Mint does stir up the minde and the taste to a greedy desire of meat'.

The constituents in the Mints, the oils and acids, are entirely beneficial in their action on the digestive organs. They stimulate the appetite, relieve flatulence and are cooling, and these virtues are to some extent made available in the mint-flavoured foods, and particularly in minty medications. Mint sauce is one of cookery's triumphs, and this is greatly improved if two kinds of Mint are used, Spearmint and Apple Mint in equal parts. To make the sauce, chop the leaves very fine, or mince them, and to every tablespoonful of chopped mint add a teaspoonful of castor sugar, or honey; let it stand for a few minutes, then just moisten the mint with a little vinegar or lemon juice. The best mint sauce is thick with mint—not just bits of it floating in vinegar.

Every garden and every cook is enriched by a choice of culinary Mints. Apart from the all-purpose common Lamb-mint, Spearmint, there is the 3-foot-tall, fruity-flavoured Apple Mint, whose rounded woolly leaves dry very well; and the Pineapple Mint, which is a low-growing herb with green leaves splashed with gold, and a fruity pineapple scent and flavour that is good in fruit salads and soft drinks. My favourite scented Mint is the Eau de Cologne, a variety of the Chartreuse, properly called *Mentha citrata*. This has dark green leaves tinged with bronze-purple, and they smell strongly of Eau de Cologne when crushed—and when dried for pot-pourri or sachets. This Mint is a delicious flavouring for an orange or lemon dessert jelly, especially one made from the fresh fruit juice: for this I boil up 1 pint of water with 6 oz sugar and the yellow peel (no white pith) from two large juicy fruits, with a good bunch of the Mint: then it stands with the lid on to infuse the flavours; 2 oz of gelatine are stirred in until dissolved. When the liquid is fairly cool it is strained; the fruit is added with a wineglassful of sherry. Then it is put to set in a mould. This jelly is also good for invalids as well as the epicures. The Pineapple Mint may be used to flavour jellies in the same way.

Mints in the garden must be given a feed of good compost each spring to encourage their best flavour. Ideally, they should be shifted to a new bed every two years. They thrive best in a well-drained soil containing plenty of humus.

Dried Mint is available at all good health stores; also Mint oils and essences.

NETTLE, STINGING NETTLE *Urtica dioica*

Nettles are another of my own favourite herbs; and they have always been eaten and drunk so long as they have grown near man's abode. Like Dandelions, Nettles were once grown in kitchen gardens to provide a spinach-like vegetable for springtime. I prefer them to spinach, and when they are cooked with Dandelion leaves the dish is really delicious. The Nettle's culinary and medicinal merits are in its constituents, and the plant's frequent use in spring and early summer can go a long way towards remedying deficiencies in our diet. Later in the season the Nettle develops crystals which are rather harmful, so that the fresh sprays

...d be used until July, then the dried herb will be needed
...the tea.

As a source of iron the Stinging Nettle exceeds most
other vegetables. It gives us vitamin C to ward off colds;
and the formic acid and phosphates, with the mineral salts
and ammonia which this plant amasses not only make it a
really valuable herbal treatment for a wide variety of ills but
also make it a great help in preventing them.

As a vegetable to be eaten through May and June, gather
a quantity of the fresh young Nettle tops—wearing gloves
and remembering that the greenery boils down considerably
to shrink the amount—wash them in several waters, put the
tops, dripping wet, into a saucepan with no more than a
tablespoonful of water to prevent their burning: add a piece
of butter and keep turning the leaves until, after a few
minutes' cooking, they are tender. Strain and chop the mass,
add salt and pepper and a little more butter, a squeeze of
lemon juice and chopped Chives or Spring Onion—with a
dash of nutmeg (which is also health-giving) to give a
piquant flavour. Like spinach, this purée makes a good base
for poached eggs—an excellent dish for a light luncheon or
for invalids—young or old. Nettles are good when cooked
with Dandelion leaves (see Dandelion).

The Nettle's medicinal uses are legion; as a stimulant; as
a remedy for many ills—and chlorophyll is generally
obtained from the plants.

The fresh tips to be served as a vegetable must come from
the garden, park or countryside not later than mid-July—

they also make the tea. But Nettle's medicinal virtues may be enjoyed at any time from the carefully dried and powdered leaves and the seeds sold by herb shops. To make the tea, use either three fresh Nettle tops about 4 inches long to 1 pint of boiling water or a flat teaspoonful of dried or powdered Nettle or seeds. This tea, taken in wineglassful doses three or four times a day, is an excellent antiscorbutic; it helps the circulation, cures nettlerash and helps to relieve gouty gravel. It helps to reduce weight, relieves asthma and bronchial coughs, and the dried leaves, burnt and inhaled, will also give relief in these bronchial ailments. Burns are quickly relieved by applying linen cloths soaked in the tea infusion—which is also an excellent gargle for a sore or relaxed throat. Nettle tea must not be brewed too strong, and it must not be drunk too frequently.

For those of us who are lucky enough to possess a garden, Nettles are wonderfully efficient activators on the compost heap; they encourage and stimulate the necessary bacteria. Also they make an effective liquid plant food if a sheaf of Nettles is left to soak for two or three weeks in a vessel filled with rain-water. And if the gardener's hair is thinning he should comb it daily with expressed Nettle juice, or make a tonic lotion by simmering a good handful of Nettle tops in a quart of water for two hours, then straining and bottling the liquid when cold—treatment for effective results—wet the scalp with the lotion and lightly massage it on alternate nights.

Nettle beer is refreshing, and it contains some of the

health-giving properties of the plant, and it can be drunk eight days after brewing. Nettle wine must mature for a year, but it is well worth anticipating.

PARSLEY   *Carum petroselinum*

Parsley's virtues are rarely appreciated: too often sprays of its bright green health-giving leaves are thought of merely to garnish dishes to tempt the diners—and too often the food they decorate is less wholesome than the parsley which is set aside. This herb has as rich a content of vitamin A as cod-liver oil—and more vitamin C than oranges; and the plant's various constituents are entirely beneficial and can function in several ways. They act as a mild aperient, they help the digestion, they are stimulating. And Parsley is particularly helpful for coping with bladder and kidney disorders, dispelling gravel, stone and kidney congestion. It also relieves dropsy and jaundice, and one of its components, *Apiol*, is used in the treatment of malaria and other diseases. Parsley tea has been used with excellent results to avoid kidney complications caused by dysentery. The bruised leaves, like those of Clover, Violet, Comfrey and Celandine, have aided herbalists' treatments for dispelling tumours.

With all these helpful qualifications for the prevention and cure of ailments, parsley deserves to be used as much as possible in the preparation of food—and it should often go into the daily herb tea, as well as the one brewed for a specific curative purpose.

The tea is infused from five good-sized fresh leaves and stems, or a teaspoonful of dried leaves or seeds—to $\frac{1}{2}$ pint of boiling water (this is also helpful for children troubled with wind).

Parsley's culinary uses are well known in soups, stews, casseroles, fish or bean sauces, omelettes and scrambled eggs, and in stuffings, also in salads, mixed green, raw vegetable, cheese and tomato, egg, fish or potato, or as a minced herb garnish over vegetables. But it is often too meanly used.

Dried Parsley and seeds are stocked by all good health food stores and herb shops, and there are decoctions available containing the valuable elements.

In the garden Parsley is a hardy biennial, and new seed should be sown each year in April and in August to keep up the supply. The plants grow best in a well-drained bed of fairly rich soil (the seeds take about six weeks to germinate).

PARSLEY PIERT   *Alchemilla arvensis*

This little wild plant has a large reputation in herbal medicine, but though it is common everywhere in the country-side, it is not showy enough to be popular among our familiar wild plants. This herb prefers a dry soil in fields, or on walls and gravel-pits, where it sits among its dusky green, deeply cut, hairy leaves, producing minute greenish, stalk-less flowers crowded into tufts which are usually hidden by

85

the foliage: the tallest Parsley Piert rarely exceeds 4 inches; otherwise it rather resembles its relation, Lady's Mantle, *Alchemilla vulgaris*.

The whole plant is used for its medicinal virtues, which are astringent, soothing to the digestive organs, and it is cooling. This Parsley breakstone's high repute is for its effect on the bladder and kidneys, for its success in removing gravel and stones. It works violently but safely by the urine, and removes obstructions of these organs—it is also recommended for treating jaundice. Some doctors recommend regular doses of the tea infusion for people who may be subject to kidney and bladder complaints, when half-teacupful doses may be taken three times a day.

The tea may be made from the herb which is stocked by herbalists—or the fresh plant (if it is known).

There is a liquid extract available—and Parsley Piert pills, which are a convenient medication, are sold in all good health food shops or herb stores.

To make the tea, allow a handful of the herb to a pint of boiling water. This acts best when infused with other herbs taken for stone; Comfrey, Marshmallow or Slippery Elm bark will soothe the passing.

WILD ROSE, DOG ROSE   *Rosa canina*
RED ROSE, PINK ROSE   *Rosa gallica*

The Rose, wild or 'tame', is the most spectacular of pleasurable herbs, and is among the most ancient of medicinal plants. The Wild Rose or Dog Rose is too well known to need any description; but the name Dog Rose is not derogatory, as 'Dog' is used for many plants. It is a corruption of dag—a dagger—in allusion to the sharp thorns. These single flowers of pink or blushing white have no honey, but are loved by bees for their pollen; and their fruits, the 'hips', hold a collection of good things which pleased the apothecary, now the herbalist, and any doctor of medicine. These fruits, when ripe and shiny-scarlet, contain such components as tannin, resin and curative acids, such as citric, malic and the ascorbic acid that is the source of vitamin C. The Rose hip products, the enjoyable syrups and conserves, are especially valuable for giving this necessary food-factor, with the other helpful Rose constituents, to children and adults.

The dried leaves of this Rose and those of other types have several medicinal properties which become available when they are made into a tea as a substitute for ordinary tea, or they may be mixed with tea. The brew cools the blood, it is soothing, it acts gently and kindly on the liver and the stomach; and it stops a tickling cough.

Almost the same claims are made for the petals of red or pink Roses, especially of the *Rosa gallica* types. The old-fashioned Apothecaries' Rose is a lovely kind for any garden, with its strongly scented deep pink flowers to provide petals to make Rose Conserve and Rose Vinegar.

The conserve is made by beating the petals to a pulp and adding three times its weight in honey or castor sugar: then thoroughly beating the mixture. This preserve, eaten in tea-spoonfuls, provides a lovely way to take a Rose treatment for an irritating cough, to strengthen the heart, the liver, the stomach, to help the digestion, and it is sufficiently astringent to stop diarrhoea.

Rose vinegar is another delightful Rose-petal possibility, for dabbing on the temples to soothe a headache, or to refresh a hot, tired, traveller. To make it, fill a jar with petals and add white or wine vinegar: leave it to soak for 24 hours, then strain. Add a fresh lot of petals to the vinegar and let it stand again. Repeat the process until the liquid is slightly oily and strongly perfumed. Strain through fine muslin and decanter into small, tightly stoppered bottles. Keep them in a dark cupboard to preserve the scent.

Rose-hip tablets, Rose-hip tea, Rose-hip syrup and Conserves, the dried petals and buds are all on sale in good health stores.

ROSEMARY   *Rosmarinus officinalis*

Rosemary, the herb sacred to remembrance, which, it was believed, strengthened the brain and the memories, the herb which symbolised friendship and love, so that it was in every bride's bouquet and a few leaves, chopped fine, went into the wedding cake, and the Christmas pudding, the stuffings and other festive dishes. The evergreen aromatic shrub should be in every garden for its scent and its dark beauty; also for the little mauve flowers beloved by bees—

and cooks for salad blossoms and conserves.

Rosemary should be available either dried or garden fresh for its other culinary uses—a sprig placed on any roasting joint adds a fine flavour; and a joint of lamb is greatly enhanced when the skin is pricked with a sharp point to allow a few of Rosemary's stiff narrow leaves to be inserted every 2 inches of the surface; the Rosemary insertions may be alternated with spikes of Garlic, pushed into such skin pockets; ready for the oven.

This herb contains valuable constituents making its effects tonic, stimulating and digestive. Rosemary tea, made by infusing a few young tops, leaves and flowers in a pint of boiling water, is an effective remedy for colds, nervous complaints, headaches, flatulence and poor circulation.

Rosemary conserve has the same curative effects, and to make this pleasant concoction, beat up the freshly cut tops with three times their weight of brown sugar or honey, and enjoy it as a sweetmeat taken in teaspoonfuls. This is comforting to coughs—and it is good as an accompaniment to meat dishes instead of currant jelly.

Rosemary has an old and proved reputation for stimulating the hair-bulbs and preventing baldness—also for beautifying the hair, and the Rosemary shampoos are available at good health stores and from the best herbalists; as are other Rosemary products.

Rosemary grows best in light, well-drained soil, in a sheltered, sunny position—and it looks beautiful when trained against a south or west wall. It is said to grow taller in a neutral soil, but it is more fragrant when grown in a chalky bed.

RUE   *Ruta graveolens*

In ancient Rome Rue was eaten in great quantities by artists to preserve their eyesight, sharpen their vision and ease eyestrain—and in most civilised places it was taken to ward off contagious diseases and to cure several ailments. And the finely chopped leaves still add their zest to Italian salads—and to mine.

In a garden Rue is a beautiful little shrub about 3 feet high, with finely cut, sea-green leaves wearing a grape-like bloom. The small flowers, borne in panicles or clusters, have pale yellow petals surrounding a gay emerald-green centre. The whole plant is aromatic, smelling to some noses of coconut or greengage plums, to others, just nasty (mine likes it). The leaves have a strange taste, rather pungent and bitter enough to make appetite-provoking sandwiches if a few are finely chopped and spread between thin slices of brown bread and butter.

Rue has an ancient and modern reputation as a disinfectant, and should be added to the herb teas when epidemics or winter colds are threatening prospects. Medicinally, it is a stimulant; it cures or wards off cramp spasms; and a warm infusion suppresses excessive menstruation. But Rue should not be taken in large doses, which are liable to cause inflammation and nerve derangement. It is a herb to be used with discretion, and then, with confidence. It contains rutin, which is now prescribed for circulatory diseases.

For definite ailments for which it is effective, the tea is infused from one teaspoonful of the dried powdered herb, or about two tips of the fresh plant, to 1 pint of boiling water: and is taken in teacupful doses. This will relieve coughs, colic, flatulence, croup and stomach upsets. A fresh leaf or two chewed will relieve a nervous headache; hysterical spasm; giddiness and palpitation—and strengthen the eyesight?

Rue is a spartan that will not tolerate pampering. It grows best and resists winter frosts when planted in poor soil.

The dried herb and oil of Rue are available at good herbal stores.

SAGE   *Salvia officinalis*

There is an old English proverb which maintains, 'He that would live for aye, must eat Sage in May.' But authorities have never limited this herb's benevolence to any month. It is always of value, whether dried, from a herb store, or fresh from the garden, where the common broad-leaved variety has the most pungent flavour in its greyish, evergreen foliage. The plant's chemical constituents, its oils, tannin and resin, are stimulating and astringent; and they are soothing to the stomach, they aid the digestion and dispel flatulence. For these qualities the herb plays an important part in cookery, especially in the stuffings and sauces to accompany such rich meats as goose, duck and pork. Pork sausages were once made more tasty and digestible when Sage (and Basil) were mixed with the meat; and this added attraction is worth the trouble of stripping our modern sausages to add the minced herbs, with care and luck the meat can be returned to the skin. One of Sage's oldest uses, and one in which it is still tasty, is to flavour cheese. This is perfect for home-made cottage, or milk, cheese, made from sour milk curds, strained through muslin, seasoned and flavoured with herbs—either mixed or an individual like Sage. The herb is also good in herb butters, and in sandwiches—a spread of the leaves minced or finely chopped.

Sage tea, an infusion made by pouring 1 pint of boiling water over one teaspoonful of dried herb—or ½ oz of fresh leaves—is an excellent remedy for weak digestion, loss of appetite, nervous debility, biliousness and upset liver, kidney trouble, internal bleeding, nervous headaches and colds. It has been known to relieve the shakings of ague and the night sweatings of tubercular patients.

This same infusion can be used to bathe bruises, ulcers, raw skin grazes and sprains, and it is an excellent gargle for sore or relaxed throats, and a help to relieve bleeding gums. And if applied to the scalp it darkens fading hair.

As a garden plant that is decorative and useful, sage likes a good lightish soil in a sunny bed that is cosily sheltered from winter winds. It lives attractively for three years, then tails off into woody, leggy growth, so that cuttings or layer-

ings should be taken from two-year-old plants, to keep up
the profitable supply.

SAVORY   SUMMER—*Satureia hortensis*
                          WINTER—*Satureia montana*

There are two popular kinds of Savory to grow in Britain;
Summer Savory, which is an annual to be sown in the
garden in early spring or to be bought dried, in packets; and
Winter Savory, a hardy perennial that is useful for several
years, until it gets too woody and leggy. Summer Savory is
the doctoring herb and the cook's favourite; Winter Savory
has little medicinal virtue beyond pleasuring the appetite
and aiding the digestion, but it is available in the garden
before Summer Savory's seeds have germinated.

Both Savorys are famous aromatic culinary herbs, and
their warm spicy scent and taste is an asset in minces, stews,
sausages, pork-pies and savoury omelettes. They are very
good inclusions in stuffing for roast pork, veal or turkey.
And in such soups as lentil, fish, bean or pea. Savory makes
the perfect flavouring for sauce served with broad beans,
and a spray should also be cooked with these beans, and
with peas, too, as a change from Mint. Savory is one of the
herbs which are relished with trout. Either finely chopped
fresh leaves or a little of the dried herb are good sprinkled
over a salad, especially one of tomato or of potato.

When dried, Summer Savory keeps its aroma and flavour
better than Winter Savory, and the dried herb is stocked by

the best herb shops ready to be enjoyed.

Medicinally, Summer Savory relieves flatulence and colic, and it is warming and easing for catarrhs and coughs. An infusion of one teaspoonful of the dried herb, or a spray from the fresh plant, with $\frac{1}{2}$ pint of boiling water may be taken in wineglassful doses for these complaints, and it is also a good lotion with which to bathe inflamed eyes.

Savory is a pleasant medication to be sometimes blended into the daily herb tea.

In appearance, Savory plants rather resemble each other. Their dark green leaves grow like Rosemary's, only they are flatter and fleshier. Winter Savory, like Rue, prefers a poor dryish soil. If it is well fed it grows too soft to withstand winter frosts.

SLIPPERY ELM   *Ulmus fulva*
                                                Ulmus rubra

The Red Elm, Indian Elm, which grows in the U.S.A. and Canada, provides one of the most valued of all herbal materials for food and medicine. This Elm is a small tree with very rough branches, long toothed and hairy leaves, and yellow woolly leaf-buds. The inner bark is the treasure collected in springtime to be dried for distribution, and great quantities of the stuff come from the State of Michigan. Slippery Elm was widely used by the Red Indians, who gave it the name 'Oohooska', it slips; this is a fair description of the bark, which is so full of mucilage that when wet it swells into a slippery jelly. In springtime, when the tree is awaking to active life, the vital elements stored in the roots through winter begin to circulate through all the structure to nourish and renew the parts: not the leaves and flowers alone but the trunk and branches are to be given their expanding girth which is building under the older bark. This new 'bark' is the busy trackway for the distribution of all the precious elements which are necessary to the Elm and desirable for ourselves. It is taken from ten-year-old trees in very thin strips about 2 inches wide and 2 feet long; and by this robbing, the tree is killed.

Of course, all trees have the same activity, but this particular Elm manufactures its peculiar effective mucilage, which is entirely soothing and healing. It can spread a fine protective and curative coating over the digestive organs, it softens and heals hardening tissue, it loosens mucus secretions in the bronchial tubes and eases their expectoration. It induces and eases the flow of urine to relieve kidney and bladder upsets. And, with all these virtues, Slippery Elm is highly nutritious, and it is easily digested by the most delicate of stomachs, from infant to aged.

Although Slippery Elm is an essential ingredient in many medications sold for various purposes, the food product is of such value as to be a household necessity. This finely powdered bark makes an excellent food or gruel for the very sick and for the invalid recovering, and for anyone troubled with acidity and upset stomach, and it is the ideal nightcap to induce peaceful sleep. It is the perfect sustenance for anybody who is too exhausted to digest an ordinary meal. It is an immediate cure for flatulence caused by nervous strain. And this food's special quality soothes and heals all parts of the body it contacts, so that it is wonderfully effective in cases of gastritis, gastric catarrh, colitis, cystisis and enteritis; and in certain conditions it is often the only food which the poorly stomach can tolerate and retain. It is excellent for relieving coughs and assuring an undisturbed night's rest. This is a perfect food for heart troubles and for pulmonary diseases.

Pure Slippery Elm bark or powder is sold for poulticing or food, and this is exceedingly useful to have in the house ready to apply to gatherings caused by thorns, stings and other things, or for burns and inflammations, and for abscesses, boils, eruptions and swollen glands. For simple needs the mixture can be placed directly on the affected part, but for more serious wounds, suppurations or abscesses it should be sandwiched between muslin, as the poultice sticks like glue. If it is to be applied to a hairy part of the body the contacting side of the muslin should be smeared with olive oil.

The food, the bark, the ointments and other products are all obtainable from herbal stores.

TANSY   *Tanacetum vulgare*

Tansy is a beautiful aromatic herb resembling a great sheaf of rich green feathers, 3 feet tall, topped in summer with dense clusters of flowers like golden Bachelor's Buttons. The spicy scent of the leaves is of sweet ginger, and they give the same delicious flavour to food. In the garden Tansy's habit is invasive, and the right way to enjoy the plant is to confine the roots within an old bottomless tub or tin bath, buried from sight: otherwise it romps over the ground with its venturesome, exploring roots. But when so restricted it can be kept as a shapely ornamental plant and the roots can be controlled. It is a hardy herbaceous perennial that will grow in any reasonably fertile soil.

Tansy has many virtues to offer us. As a culinary herb it has an ancient reputation for flavouring cakes and puddings—to be eaten at Easter time to purify the body after the salt-fish diet of Lent. I use the juice from leaves pounded in a mortar to flavour a ground-rice pudding, or baked egg custard, or sweet omelettes. And there are several old-fashioned recipes for puddings and fritters that are deliciously flavoured with Tansy juice. The tender young leaves of Tansy and Rosemary minced together are a delicate flavouring for pastry or biscuits. And two or three finely chopped young leaves are nice sprinkled over a salad, or blended in stuffings. A Tansy leaf or two will also enrich a meat or vegetable soup or stew.

Apart from its fragrant flavour, other reasons for using Tansy are for its various constituents, the oils, fats, resins, acids, tannin, citrates and other efficacious principles—which are curative for many ailments, and a protection against ill-health. Tansy is tonic, stimulating and healing. It is prescribed for weakness of the kidneys, for promoting perspirations to sweat-out cold, chill or influenza, it reduces feverishness, it helps the digestion and avoids flatulence. It will put right an upset stomach and cope with colic and with cramp spasms. This is a herb particularly beneficial for female disorders, as it acts directly on the womb, and will quieten attacks of nausea or hysteria.

The infusion of one teaspoonful of dried Tansy, or about five fresh leaves, to 1 pint of boiling water makes the tea for all internal requirements, and it should be taken in wine-glassful doses repeated fairly frequently. A Tansy leaf should also go into the daily herb tea two or three times a week for ordinary drinking.

A hot infusion used as a fomentation will relieve a sprain, and the pain from a rheumatic part. An infusion of a half to one teaspoonful of dried flowers or seeds, with 1 pint of water, if taken two or three times a day, is a good remedy for attacks of gout.

Tansy's properties are very potent, and it should not be taken in excessive doses.

The dried herb, flowers and seeds are available from good herb stores.

TARRAGON *Artemisia dracunculus*

Tarragon, the little dragon, is one of the most popular culinary herbs on the Continent, where it is particularly appreciated for flavouring chicken dishes. It makes the delicious vinegar that is the only correct flavouring for tartare sauce, and a tasty vinegar for French salad dressing and mayonnaise, also for mixing mustard. To make this, gather the leaves on a dry sunny day in July, put 2 oz of leaves in a bottle and cover with a pint of white wine, or white malt vinegar. Cork well, and leave for a month before straining and rebottling. My own supplies of this herb are usually too limited to allow for this mixture—so that I push a couple of good sprays into a pint bottle of white vinegar and leave it until the herb loses its colour, and the result is equally good.

Tarragon's warm flavour is appetising in salads. It is one of the proper herbs for the French Bouquet Garni. It goes well into fish stuffings, and is a tasty garnish-sprinkling for shellfish.

This herb's volatile essential oil, which is identical with that of Anise, is best in the dried herb. Medicinally, Tarragon is cordial to the heart, the liver and to the brain, so that apart from its flavour it can also add value to the dishes it flavours.

Tarragon is a 'must' in any herb bed, where its fresh leaves are at hand for the cook. But it is not an easy plant to grow—I have to renew my own bed quite often, but in one garden I know, it grows like a weed. New plants should be set in April in a well-drained bed, in a sunny sheltered position.

The plants must be bought from a reputable herb nursery, and they must be French Tarragon. Some nurseries sell Russian Tarragon, which is useless as a culinary herb. The

French is *Artemisia dracunculus*, the Russian is *Artemisia dracunculoides*, and this grows like a willow tree and lacks the Tarragon flavour.

Dried Tarragon is stocked by herb shops, and the fresh sprays are sold by the best greengrocers.

THYME   *Thymus vulgaris*

Thyme is a generous herb, but nowadays is so meanly used that we seldom benefit from its possible virtues. The few dried or fresh leaves in our occasional stuffings, or sprays in the Bouquet Garni, show our ignorance of this herb's true qualities. We have degraded it to a mere flavouring herb, whereas all the varieties of Thyme have their curative gifts for our well-being. Thyme's constituents, phenol, thymol and other elements, are antiseptic, soothing to the stomach and digestive organs, and they prevent gastric fermentation, and so dispel wind and colic, also they are stimulating. Medicinally, Thyme is used for nervous distresses arising from the organs of reproduction, in both sexes, and it has long been the herb particularly beneficial to the womb in its troubles. The thymol is the ancient and modern enemy of catarrh and of throat infections, and it is a basic ingredient in many medications.

The pounded fresh leaves, or dried ones, from 1 to 3 oz mixed with honey and taken daily, is considered to be a safe cure for whooping cough: and the tea infused from one teaspoonful of dried Thyme, or fresh Thyme to a pint of boiling water and sweetened with honey, is also recommended for the same complaint—and for all the other ailments I have mentioned. It will help to promote perspiration at the beginning of a cold, and will help in any feverish complaint.

The ancient Athenians and Romans knew and exploited the qualities of Thyme and grew vast areas of the herb to serve the double purpose of a supply for kitchens and physicians, and for the flowers to feed the bees which were pastured among it and would give the particular flavour to their honey. The best Thyme honey came from Mount Hymettus, near Athens—and it still does.

Thyme's numerous culinary uses include flavouring for soups, stews, casseroles, stuffings, minces, savoury egg dishes, salads, and garnishes for potatoes, leeks, broad beans and carrots. Beef for roasting should be rubbed with Thyme and carry a sprinkling of it into the oven. It is excellent with goose, duck, hare, chicken and turkey; and in herb butters and, especially, cheese.

At least two varieties should be available in every garden; the Black or Common Thyme, *Thymus vulgaris*, and Lemon-scented Thyme, *T. citriodorus*. They are easy to grow in a sunny position, in light gritty soil.

The dried herb is available from all good herb stores.

YARROW   *Achillea millefolium*

Yarrow, Milfoil, Thousandleaf, is a very familiar wild plant and garden weed, with dark green, fine, ferny leaves and flat masses of tiny white- or pink-tinted flowers. And it is a medicinal herb that is helpful enough to be sold by herbalists and to be incorporated into some of their medications.

Yarrow's several constituents are oil, resin, tannin, gum, phosphates, chlorides of lime and potash (also a peculiarly potent principle), and, with its rich copper accumulation, these make it particularly effective for the treatment of several ailments. It provides a valuable domestic remedy for promoting perspiration to relieve a feverish cold. An infusion of 1 oz of the fresh herb or a teaspoonful of the dried (obtainable from a good herbal store) is made with 1 pint of boiling water. This tea forms a rapid cure for influenza when it is combined with elderflowers and peppermint, a pinch of cayenne pepper and a little honey, and it should be taken warm in wineglassful doses, with a teaspoonful of Composition Essence added to each dose. This remedy is so effective that the dried ingredients and the essence should be kept handy for winter's ills of colds and chills and attacks of flu. This same concoction is useful, too, for children's colds and for measles and other eruptive, spotty, diseases.

The tea infusion of Yarrow, straight, without the extras added for colds, etc., is recommended for rheumatism, and for kidney disorders.

Yarrow's astringent properties are very effective in coping with bleeding wounds, and the tea used as a lotion will quickly heal them. It is employed for bleeding piles, and, as a bonus, Yarrow tea can be used as a hair-rinse to prevent baldness.

HEALTH FROM FLOWERS
HONEY, POLLEN, SEEDS

Many flowers are edible and entirely beneficial. They may contain some of the virtues of their parent plant, and some have other qualities which are entirely their own, and with a few exceptions they all have the stores of delectable nutrients to feed the insects they must attract to fertilise the seeds. Certain moths can serve this purpose, but so far as we are concerned, bees are their most important lovers. Flowers have inviting scented oils in their petals to advertise their location and to titillate the visitor's appetite for the nectar and pollen. The bees take home the nectar in sacs to transform into honey for their young and for the hive's winter food store. The honey will keep as purest food, energy-giving and protective. It does not decay because it is so strong a disinfectant that no bacteria or germ could live in it (this is one of the good reasons why honey should go into the herb teas infused to cure our infections).

Bees eat the flower pollen, their 'bee-bread', of which each bloom has an ample supply for its own use and to spare. As the bees scrabble about in the ecstasy of extracting the nectar, treading the pollen-loaded anthers they automatically place enough of the fertilising grains on the particular organ of the flower to pollinate the seeds. And they amass pollen grains on their busy little legs, and like thickly padded knickerbockers they carry this precious food back to the hive and there, until recent successful experiments, pollen has remained the bees' own business and advantage.

As flowers secrete oils in their petals and are the natural source of much goodness, the Japanese and other people still make lovely flower salads, including the much-fancied, tangy-flavoured Chrysanthemum petals and the more delicate Sweet Pea and fruit blossoms. And once upon a time flowers were usual in British culinary achievements. They went into, and decorated, most mixed or fruit salads. The blooms were scattered over many a dish, savoury or sweet, and they, too, were eaten. Deftly placed floral arrangements inside jellies for festive occasions were a good cook's pride. Flowers made delicious conserves, and there was Rose-petal jam. Wines and cordials were made from flowers and, as today, they were ingredients for effective cosmetics, creams, toilet waters and vinegars. Countless blooms or petals were candied for winter enjoyment as sweetmeats, and for edible decorations on cakes, puddings and creamy desserts. We are the poorer for having lost confidence in the beneficence of natural flowers.

It would be fatuous for one to suggest that we use flowers as lavishly as our ancestors employed them—we would be puzzled to find the quantities they collected for their/many purposes. But I can suggest that when flowers are in the garden some of them should go into the kitchen for several pleasurable and profitable uses—a few of which I have given in the description of different plants—such as in salads, fruit cups, as garnishing on sauce-covered dishes. Not all flowers are suitable, but an absolutely safe choice of health-giving whole blooms can include those of the aromatic herbs, such as Lavender, Rosemary, Hyssop, Rue, Thyme, Mints, Sages, Marjoram, Savory, the whole blooms of the more showy Violet, Viola, Pansy, Borage, Comfrey, Anchusa, Lily-of-the-valley, Primrose, Cowslip, the tangy Nasturtium, Pot Marigold and Dandelion, the delicate Sweet Pea, Bean-flowers, and the petals of fruit blossoms, of Roses, clove-tasting Carnations and Pinks. This is a conservative list, but unless plants are known, it is better to be this cautious. For instance, the pollen of the Tiger Lily is poisonous.

Conserves of flowers—the old-fashioned curative delicacies are not difficult to make—with a pestle and mortar—although the once favourite Violet Conserve would require more blooms than most of us could easily muster. But conserves made of scented Rose petals, of Lavender flowers or 'pips' or of the tender green tips of Rosemary or those of the various Mints should be possible.

To make the conserve, pound the flowers or green tips to a pulp, then add three times its weight in honey—most recipes give white sugar, but I prefer to use a mild honey that is not too highly flavoured—beat the pulp and honey together before potting into little jars. The conserve is eaten in small teaspoonfuls.

Rose Hip Conserve, containing the now famous virtues

of the hips and of honey, is available ready made from health food shops. This is an asset, as preparing Rose hips is a wearying job, and they are so astringent that in my own experience they will deaden the finger-tips for a week.

We get the flowers' nectar from Honey. This is the natural sugar the body requires rather than the over-refined, depleted, white sugar which is too often consumed. White sugar is an exhausted product that can be harmful in its power to kill certain vitamins and other essentials, which honey actually preserves and helps. Honey is a source of the energy created by natural sugar. When it is taken from bees that have been pastured on particular crops the honey will contain some of the desirable qualities of these flowers, such as Clover; Thyme, the Greek honey Hymettus; Lime blossom, Orange and other fruit blossoms, or Heather—all of which give the bees' product a distinctive taste. For these attributes I think these special honeys, pure and un-adulterated, should be chosen to enrich the herb teas infused for specific purposes, or for general well-being, in preference to the ordinary undistinguished honeys that are often adulterated with sugar—or produced from sugar-fed bees. Lime-blossom honey is the most valued of all honeys, both for its flavour and for medicinal purposes.

Pollen, so far as humans are concerned, has been princi-pally notorious for giving many of us hay-fever, and a rash. Its rewarding virtues were the bees' prerogative and beyond our reach until fairly recently. But now, by a complicated process of intensive production, extraction and elimination of the factors to which many people were allergic, pollen has been made to yield its recuperative and highly invigorating substance, which is called *Cernitin*. This further enlarges our scope for enjoying the real health-giving possibilities that flowers can offer. The pollen-based commodities are now obtainable in several forms, as tablets, a tonic wine and the natural extract.

Seeds in some form are a necessity in our healthy diets. Their production is the most important of all a plant's efforts—to the plant and to man—all the energy a plant expends is primarily generated towards the ultimate production of its 'young'. The wonderful mechanism of the flower, which not only equips it to deal with the process in all its stages but to actually attract the bees, or other means, to fulfil the purpose of fertilisation of the 'fruits', its offspring. And when this is completed the seed-cases, of highly specialised material, are stocked with the essentials for their germination and for the primary nourishment of the baby 'sprouts' until they are strong enough to grow roots to seek their own sustenance. Thus, the seeds are packages containing the germ of life and very special concentrates. The bulk of human food comes from the seeds of wheat, with other corns and cereals.

As a herb fancier, I am concerned with the probable disastrous results caused by modern methods of maltreating these precious cereal seeds. The widely advertised 'refined' white flours have to be robbed of the valuable gluten and of the very 'germ' for which flour qualified as a basic food; and this lack, plus the presence of some chemical agent used in the bleaching and refining process, is even more true of the popular super-sifted products. I may be super-sensitive, as when I used one of these bodiless, ethereal types and while weighing and mixing it into the cake batter, the particles puffed up into the air and gave me hay fever, a prickly sore throat and prickling swollen lips. If breathing the stuff will do this damage I wonder what happens when it is eaten! I have since heard that this effect is not uncommon.

We are vulnerable to yet another danger with modern flours—and with other commercially grown food-plants— through the really poisonous or very questionable pesticides with which the crops are sprayed. The safest and most nutritious flours available today, the wholemeal and other finer types, and flours milled from various cereals, are found in the ranges sold by health food shops and other good stores that carry similar stocks. We can be especially confident in those named products which bear the assurance of being unsprayed and organically or compost grown. These will be clean and wholesome, hale and hearty, from good feeding and knowledgeable husbandry.

The regular use of a really good flour that is vouched for is a long-term health insurance; but the immediate and considerable benefits from the heart of the Wheat are provided by the energising *Wheat Germ* products containing, undiminished, the valuable vitamins B1, B2 and E.

Seeds come into a healthy diet in many forms, and apart from various cereals, nuts and vegetable seeds such as peas, beans, etc., there are the important oily seeds which give us the special margarines and cooking oils to replace the acid animal fats such as butter and lard. These are sometimes difficult for many people to digest—and, it seems, are also becoming possible health hazards through the milk retention of penicillin with which cows are treated—and DDT picked up from pesticide sprays.

The worthy seed-oil products come from several sources such as the golden Maize corn, Linseed, from the bright blue-flowered Flax plant, the giant yellow Sunflower's seeds and the seeds of Safflower. This versatile plant has long supplied excellent seed oil for cooking in China, India, Egypt and Southern Europe, and its flowers as medicine for children's complaints have been used everywhere. The flowers have been valued in the East as a splendid dye for colouring silken textiles yellow, red, rose or scarlet; and mixed with finely powdered talc they make the well-known 'rouge' to give the added blush to many a cheek.

I have included this bit of colourful information because some people I know have thought 'Safflower' was another name for 'Sunflower' products; and I am sure there are readers who, like myself, prefer to know what they are eating.

Before leaving the subject of seeds—which if I had adequately covered it would have filled a large book—I must mention my own much-liked Poppy seeds. These tasty little purple dots are too often suspected of containing the morphine drug for which their parents are famed, but they are innocent babes, packed with a curative and nutritious fine oil. They may be ground up to put into cakes as they are used on the Continent and in India, or they can be left whole and scattered over cakes or bread before baking, to add their delicious nutty flavour, and their health-giving properties.

HERBS TO RELIEVE OR AVOID MANY ILLS

ABSCESSES. Burdock, Chamomile, Charcoal, Chickweed, Comfrey, Ground Ivy, Slippery Elm.

ACIDITY. Charcoal, Dandelion, Slippery Elm.

ACNE. Agrimony, Burdock, Comfrey, Dandelion, Kelp, Nettle.

ADOLESCENT SPOTS. Agrimony, Charcoal, Comfrey, Goose-grass.

AGUES. Avens, Sage.

ANAEMIA. Cicely, Clover, Comfrey, Dandelion, Kelp, Nettle.

APPETITE LOSS. Balm, Bay, Chamomile, Chives, Mint, Sage.

ARTERIES, HARDENING. Buckwheat (Rutin), Chlorophyll, Dandelion, Lime flowers, Rue.

ARTHRITIS, RHEUMATOID. Comfrey, Dandelion.

ASTHMA. Coltsfoot, Comfrey, Garlic, Hyssop, Marjoram, Nettle.

BILIOUSNESS. Buchu, Dandelion, Groundsel.

BLADDER DISORDERS. Buchu, Burdock, Couch-grass, Dandelion, Elder, Goutweed, Ground Ivy, Hawthorn, Lily-of-the-valley, Lovage, Parsley, Parsley Piert, Slippery Elm.

BLOOD DISORDERS. Buckwheat (Rutin), Chlorophyll, Comfrey, Dandelion, Hawthorn, Lime flowers, Rosemary.

BOILS. Chamomile, Charcoal, Chickweed, Comfrey, Burdock, Ground Ivy, Slippery Elm, Yarrow.

BRAIN, STIMULANTS FOR WEAKENING MEMORY. Cowslip, Dill, Lily-of-the-valley, Tarragon.

BROKEN BONES. Comfrey.

BRONCHIAL COMPLAINTS. Angelica, Aniseed, Borage, Cicely, Coltsfoot, Comfrey, Elder, Garlic, Hyssop, Mallow, Nettle, Slippery Elm.

BRUISES. Burdock, Comfrey, Elder, Hyssop, Lavender, Sage.

BURNS. Comfrey, Lavender, Slippery Elm.

CARBUNCLES. Charcoal, Chickweed, Comfrey, Slippery Elm.

CATARRH. Aniseed, Avens, Balm, Borage, Cicely, Clover, Coltsfoot, Elder, Savory, Thyme.

CHILBLAINS. Buckwheat (Rutin), Chickweed.

CHILLS. Hyssop, Tansy.

CIRCULATION. Buckwheat (Rutin), Comfrey, Dandelion, Hawthorn, Rosemary.

COLDS. Agrimony, Coltsfoot, Elder, Goose-grass, Hyssop, Sage, Tansy, Thyme.

COLIC. Angelica, Chamomile, Lavender, Lovage, Marjoram, Rue, Savory, Tansy.

COMPLEXION DISORDERS. Agrimony, Charcoal, Chickweed, Comfrey, Dandelion, Elder, Groundsel.

COUGHS. Agrimony, Angelica, Cicely, Coltsfoot, Ground Ivy, Hyssop, Nettle, Rue, Savory.

CRAMPS. Clover, Cowslip, Lavender, Tansy.

CROUP. Buckwheat, Rue.

CYSTITIS. Buchu, Couch-grass, Comfrey, Mallow.

DIARRHOEA. Agrimony, Avens, Comfrey, Goose-grass, Lime flowers.

DIGESTION UPSETS—DYSPEPSIA, INDIGESTION. Angelica, Aniseed, Avens, Basil, Bay, Borage, Balm, Burdock, Caraway, Chamomile, Charcoal, Chives, Dill, Fennel, Garlic, Hyssop, Marjoram, Mints, Parsley, Parsley Piert, Tansy, Thyme.

DROPSICAL CONDITIONS. Chamomile, Garlic, Parsley, Parsley Piert.

DYSENTERY. Avens, Comfrey, Mallow.

ECZEMA. Agrimony, Burdock, Comfrey, Dandelion, Elder, Goutweed.

EYES, SORE, TIRED. Chickweed, Elder, Mallow, Rue, Savory.

FEVERISHNESS—FEVERISH COLDS, CHILLS, INFLUENZA. Angelica, Avens, Balm, Basil, Borage, Elder, Lovage, Tansy, Thyme, Yarrow.

FOOT DISCOMFORT. Lavender.

GOITRE. Kelp, Seaweed.

GOUT. Burdock, Couch-grass, Goutweed, Ground Ivy, Nettle, Tansy.

GRAVEL STONE. Buchu, Couch-grass, Nettle, Parsley, Parsley Piert, Slippery Elm.

HAIR CONDITIONERS. Nettle, Rosemary, Sage.

HEART WEAKNESS—PALPITATIONS. Angelica, Balm, Buckwheat (Rutin), Cicely, Dandelion, Hawthorn, Lavender, Rose, Rue, Tarragon.

HEADACHES. Lavender, Marjoram, Rosemary, Sage.

HIGH BLOOD PRESSURE. Buckwheat (Rutin), Garlic.

INDIGESTION. *See* Digestion herbs.

INFLAMMATIONS. Comfrey, Dandelion, Hawthorn, Lily-of-the-valley, Mallow, Slippery Elm.

INFLUENZA. *See* Feverishness.

INSECT BITES. Comfrey, Lavender, Lovage.

INSOMNIA. Chamomile, Cowslip, Lime flowers, Rosemary, Slippery Elm.

INTESTINAL TROUBLES. Comfrey, Mallow, Slippery Elm.

JAUNDICE. Couch-grass, Ground Ivy, Lovage, Parsley, Parsley Piert, Yarrow.

KIDNEY DISORDERS. Agrimony, Angelica, Borage, Buchu, Burdock, Couch-grass, Dandelion, Elder, Goose-grass, Goutweed, Ground Ivy, Hawthorn, Lily-of-the-valley, Lovage, Nettle, Parsley, Parsley Piert, Sage, Slippery Elm, Yarrow.

LASSITUDE. *See* Vitality herbs.

LEUCORRHOEA. Avens, Tansy, Thyme.

LIVER UPSETS. Avens, Borage, Cicely, Dandelion, Goose-grass, Rose, Tarragon.

LUNG TROUBLES. Elder, Ground Ivy, Hyssop, Sage, Slippery Elm.

MEASLES. Elder, Yarrow.

MENSTRUAL EXCESSES. Buckwheat (Rutin), Rue, Thyme.

MENSTRUAL PAINS. Lovage, Tansy, Thyme.

MUMPS. Clover.

MUSCULAR RHEUMATISM. Comfrey, Couch-grass, Cowslip, Elder, Garlic, Mallow.

NAILS, FINGER AND TOE. Kelp, Seaweed.

NAUSEA. Chamomile, Dandelion, Tansy.

NEPHRITIS. Buchu, Couch-grass.

NERVOUS DISORDERS. Basil, Caraway, Chamomile, Cowslip, Marjoram, Rosemary, Sage, Thyme.

OBESITY, OVERWEIGHT. Chickweed, Fennel, Goose-grass, Kelp, Seaweed.

PALPITATIONS. Balm, Cicely, Lavender.

PALSY. Lavender, Marjoram.

PARALYSIS. Cowslip, Lavender, Marjoram.

PILES. Chickweed.

PILES, BLEEDING. Goose-grass, Yarrow.

PLEURISY. Angelica, Cicely.

PROSTATIC SWELLINGS. Buchu.

PRURITIS. Comfrey, Marshmallow.

PSORIASIS. Goose-grass.

QUINSY. Comfrey, Thyme.

RHEUMATISM. Angelica, Burdock, Comfrey, Couch-grass, Cowslip, Elder, Goutweed, Hyssop, Kelp, Mallow, Marjoram, Seaweed, Yarrow.

SCIATICA. Goutweed, Ground Ivy.

SCROFULA. Goose-grass.

SCURVY. Chickweed, Dandelion, Goose-grass.

SKIN ERUPTIONS. Agrimony, Burdock, Charcoal, Chickweed, Elder, Goose-grass.

SLEEPLESSNESS. Chamomile, Cowslip, Lime flowers, Rosemary, Slippery Elm.

SPASMS. Clover, Cowslip, Lavender, Tansy.

SPRAINS. Comfrey, Mallow, Lavender.

STOMACH UPSETS. Borage, Buchu, Buckwheat, Chamomile, Charcoal, Cicely, Dandelion, Dill, Garlic, Lovage, Rose.

STRAINED MUSCLES AND SINEWS. Comfrey, Mallow.

SWELLINGS. Borage, Buchu, Comfrey.

THROAT TROUBLES. Agrimony, Avens, Elder, Hawthorn, Sage, Thyme.

THYROID ABNORMALITIES. Kelp, Seaweed.

ULCERS. Comfrey, Slippery Elm.

ULCERS, DUODENAL. Comfrey, Slippery Elm.

URETHRITIS, INFLAMMATION OF THE URINE TUBE. Buchu, Comfrey, Lily-of-the-valley, Mallow.

VARICOSE VEINS. Buckwheat (Rutin), Lime flowers.

VITALITY, LOSS OF. Angelica, Borage, Caraway, Dill, Hawthorn, Hyssop, Lavender, Nettle, Rosemary, Rue, Sage, Tansy, Thyme.

WHEEZING, DIFFICULT BREATHING. Coltsfoot, Comfrey.

WHOOPING COUGH. Clover, Garlic.

WOMB, HERBS DIRECTLY AFFECTING. Buckwheat (Rutin), Rue, Tansy, Thyme.

WOUNDS. Avens, Comfrey, Yarrow.

The particular parts of the herbs—as leaves, seeds—and the methods of their use for specific ailments are given with each plant in its text.

I have included Charcoal in this list of curative herbs because I have found by wide experience that the regular use of the pure carbon cleanses the blood of impurities and the stomach of acids and fermenting foodstuffs. It is a wonderful aid in the clearing of spots, abscesses, gatherings, slow-healing wounds or festers. Charcoal tablets are sold by good health food stores, and by some chemists.

HERBS AND PROPRIETARY PRODUCTS

The dried herbs for infusions—and for culinary uses—are available from most good health food stores. Their principal source of supply is:

Culpeper House Ltd.,
21, Bruton Street,
London, W.1.

Heath & Heather Ltd.,
St. Albans,
Hertfordshire.

Proprietary Products. There are hundreds on the market, but the following list is confined to the products made from the particular curative herbs I have described in the book. These are all sold by health food stores.

BUCHU
   Herbs and Pills   Heath & Heather
   Leaves   Culpeper House
BUCKWHEAT
   Rutilene Tablets   Rutin Products
   Rutin-T for infusion   ,,   ,,
   Rutivite Tablets   ,,   ,,
   Buckwheat Flour   Lima Natural Products
   Buck-Rutin Tablets   Biofoods
   Burdock and Chicory Tea   Lima Natural Products
   Chamomile Tisane   Modern Health Products

CHAMOMILE

Belgian Camomile Tisane	Culpeper House
German Camomile Tisane	„ „
Chamomile Tisane	Heath & Heather
Chamomile Tisane	Page's

CHARCOAL

Tablets	Heath & Heather; Culpeper House

CHLOROPHYLL

Tablets	Heath & Heather; Culpeper House

COMFREY

Tablets	Culpeper House
Tablets, Comfrey and Seaweed Spread	Rayner & Pennycook
Tablets	Mrs. P. Greer*
Leaf Tea	„ „
Stem Tea	„ „
Powder	„ „
Root Powder	„ „
Cream	„ „
Improved Comfrey ointment and other products	Henry Doubleday Research Association †

COWSLIP FLOWER

Tisane	Culpeper House

* Brickwall Farm, Layer de la Haye, Nr. Colchester, Essex.
† Bocking, Braintree, Essex.

DANDELION

Coffee   Heath & Heather
'Cafdan' Instant Coffee   ,,   ,,
Dandelion Essence   ,,   ,,
Dandex   Lane's
Dandex Instant   ,,
Dandex Essence   ,,
Dendelio   Lima Natural Products
Thomson's   Potter & Clarke
Dandelion Coffee (Instant)   Symington's
'Biogold' Dandelion   Hofels

ELDERFLOWER

Elderflower, Peppermint
   and Composition
   Essence   Culpeper House
Elderflower, Peppermint
   and Warming Essence   Heath & Heather
Elderflower, Peppermint
   Composition Essence   Potter's

FLOURS, COMPOST GROWN

Wholemeal, Unrefined,
   Stone Ground, etc.   Allinson's
Buckwheat   Lima Natural Products
Wholemeal, Unbleached,
   etc.   Prewett's
Soya   ,,
Soya   Soya Foods

FLOWERS
Flower Power (natural
   extract)   'Cernelle' of Sweden;
                                   Alfonal

GARLIC
Garlic Perles	Lusty's
Garlic Powder	,,
Garlic Tablets	Culpeper House
Garlic Capsules	Heath & Heather
Garlic Pearles	Hofels Ltd.
Garlic and Parsley Tablets	,,
Garlisol Tablets	Garlisol
Garlisol Liquid	,,
Garlic Ointment	,,
Garlisol Cough Mixture	,,
Garlicaps—Capsules	Biofoods

HONEYS
Clovers and various	White Gate
Clovers, Hymettus, Lime Blossom, etc.	Heath & Heather
Clovers, Hymettus, Lime Blossom, Buckwheat, etc.	Ratcliffe Bros.
Clovers, Hymettus, Lime Blossom, etc.	A. S. Rowse

KELP
Neptune's Bounty	London Health Centre
Tablets	Heath & Heather; Health Crafts

Granules, Tablets, Powder, Capsules	Lusty's
Tablets	Potter's
Ocean Bounty Tablets	Apothecary Cathay
Wild Ocean Kelp	Rational Diet

LIME FLOWERS

Lime Blossom Tea	Culpeper House
Limeflower Tisane	Heath & Heather
Lime (Tilleul) Tisane	Page's Tisanes
Lime Blossom Tisane	Modern Health Products

MARSHMALLOW

Marshmallow Lotion	Heath & Heather
Marshmallow and Slippery Elm Ointment	Culpeper House

NETTLE

Biogold Nettle	Hofels

OILS

Safflower	Alfonal; Lane's; Granose; Rational Diet
Sunflower Seed	Alfonal; Health Supply; Potter's; Culpeper House
Sunflower Oil, Safflower Oil, Capsules	Rayner & Pennycook; Lane's
Olive Oil	Costa & Co.; Culpeper House

Wheat Germ Oil	Lane's; Ritters; Health-crafts
Wheat Germ Capsules	Lane's; Hofels Ltd.; Heath & Heather; Lusty's; Potter's
Maizy Corn Oil Products	Alfonal
Linseed Products	Rayner & Pennycook
Linomel and Fluzzelin	,, ,,
Linusit Food	Sunprod Sales
Mazola Corn Oil	Brown & Polson
Walnut Oil	Sunprod Sales
Corn Oil	Culpeper House
Soya Bean Oil	,, ,,

PARSLEY PIERT

Pills	Heath & Heather

POLLEN

Pollitabs Tablets	Alfonal
Cernelle Special Tablets	,,
Cervoti Tablets	,,
Cernivin Tonic Wine	,,
Cermifex Tablets	,,
Flower Pollen Tablets	Heath & Heather
Breakfast Flakes	British Weleda

ROSE HIPS

Tablets	Healthcrafts; Hofels; Lusty's; Potter's; Rayner & Pennycook; Culpeper House

'Biogold'	Hofels Ltd.
Tisane	Modern Health Products
Rose Hip Soup	Trustin Kerwood
Syrup	Paines & Byrnes; Lane's
Liquid	Ulster Vitamins
Rose Hip and Honey Jelly	,, ,,
Spread	,, ,,
Conserve	Prewett's
Jam	A.A. Supply
Rose Hip Jelly	Lane's
Preserve	Costa & Co.
Rose Hip Tea	Culpeper House

SEAWEED

Special Preparation	Heath & Heather
Seaweed Supplement	Culpeper House
Tablets	Lusty's
Seaweed Bath Emulsion	Scottish Seabaths
Dehydrated Bags for Bath	Lusty's

SEEDS

Buckwheat	Hofels
Millet	,,
Rice	,,
Sesame and various others	,,

SLIPPERY ELM

Tablets	Heath & Heather; Lusty's
Slippery Elm and Marsh- mallow Ointment	Culpeper House
Powder	,, ,,

Food	Heath & Heather;
	Potter & Clarke;
	Lane's

YARROW
  Biogold   Hofels

There are ranges of excellent cosmetics and soaps made
from Elder Blossoms, Nettles and other effective flowers
and herbs by such makers as: Culpeper House, British
Weleda, Heath & Heather, Lusty's, Charles Perry
Cosmetics, Lane Health Products, with more to choose
from health food store stocks.

HERB PLANTS FOR THE GARDEN

For healthy plants grown in proper compost and well
packed for travel I recommend:

> E. & A. Evetts,
>   Ashfields Herb Nursery,
>   Hinstock,
>   Market Drayton,
>   Shropshire.

This nursery supplies the Apothecary's Rose and the
lovely pink-and-white-striped Rosa Mundi. Also seeds of
annual and biennial herbs and of a selected large-leaved
Dandelion for cultivation.

REFERENCES

A Modern Herbal, M. Grieve (Hafner Publishing Co. Ltd., New York).

Green Medicine, Mrs. C. F. Leyel (Faber & Faber Ltd., London).

Potter's New Cyclopaedia of Botanical Drugs and Preparations, R. C. Wren (Health Science Press, Ruslington, Sussex).

How to Enjoy Your Weeds, Audrey Wynne Hatfield (Frederick Muller, London).

Culinary and Salad Herbs, Eleanour Sinclair Rohde (Country Life Ltd., London).

Flora of the British Isles, A. R. Clapham, T. G. Tutin and E. F. Warburg (Cambridge University Press).

CORGI MINI-BOOKS

continued

	76076 5	A PARENT'S GUIDE TO SEX EDUCATION	
		Claire Rayner, S.R.N.	2/6 (12½p)
	76072 2	HOME NURSING AND FAMILY HEALTH	
		Claire Rayner, S.R.N.	3/– (15p)
	76046 3	HOUSEWORK—THE EASY WAY	
		Claire Rayner, S.R.N.	2/6 (12½p)
	76058 7	DRESSMAKING—THE EASY WAY	
		Marion Rotter	2/6 (12½p)
	76318 7	HANDWRITING Dorothy Sara	2/6 (12½p)
	76347 0	SHAPE UP TO BEAUTY Helen Speed	3/– (15p)
	76053 6	THE THOUGHTFUL GIFT BUYER'S GUIDE	
		Roma Thewes	2/6 (12½p)
	76322 5	NAME YOUR SON Roma Thewes	3/– (15p)
	76323 3	NAME YOUR DAUGHTER Roma Thewes	3/– (15p)
	76354 3	PATIENCE CARD GAMES FOR ALL THE	
		FAMILY Wendy Riches and Roma Thewes	3/– (15p)
	76361 6	COLLECTING SILVER AND PLATE	
		Guy Williams	3/– (15p)
	76357 8	COLLECTING VICTORIANA Guy Williams	3/– (15p)
	76057 9	HOMEMADE WINE Rex Tremlett	3/– (15p)
	76097 8	CREAM WITH EVERYTHING Lorna Walker	2/6 (12½p)
	76048 X	THE HOME-LOVER'S GUIDE TO ANTIQUES	
		AND BRIC-A-BRAC Guy Williams	3/– (15p)
	76049 8	DESIGN GUIDE TO HOME DECORATING	
		Guy Williams	2/6 (12½p)
	76321 7	COLLECTING CHEAP CHINA AND GLASS	
		Guy Williams	2/6 (12½p)
	76356 X	PALMISTRY Joyce Wilson	3/– (15p)
	76316 0	DOWN LEFT WITH FEELING—THE UNPAID	
		ACTOR'S HANDBOOK John Woodnutt	2/6 (12½p)
	76328 4	A CAREER FOR YOUR SON Henry Woolland	2/6 (12½p)
	76345 4	THE MAGIC OF HERBS Audrey Wynne-Hatfield	3/– (15p)

*All these books are available at your local bookshop or newsagent; or can be ordered
direct from the publisher. Just tick the titles you want and fill in the form below.*

CORGI BOOKS, Cash Sales Department, P.O. Box 11, Falmouth, Cornwall.
Please send cheque or postal order. No currency, and allow 9d (4p) per book to cover
the cost of postage and packing in U.K., 1/– (6p) per copy overseas.

NAME ....

ADDRESS ....

....